SCIENCE IN OUR WORLD

REFERENCE GUIDE

Master Glossary & Index

to volumes 1 to 29 in the

Atlantic Europe Science Library

National Curriculum Science AT1-4	AT1 Skills	AT2 Life and living processes				AT3 Materials				AT4 Physical processes				
Book	Skills	Strand 1 — Life processes, living things	Strand 2 — Variation and inheritance	Strand 3 — Populations and human influences	Strand 4 — Energy flows, matter cycles	Strand 1 — Properties and structure of materials	Strand 2 — Particle nature of materials	Strand 3 — Chemical changes	Strand 4 — Earth and atmosphere	Strand 1 — Electricity and magnetism	Strand 2 — Energy	Strand 3 — Forces	Strand 4 — Light and sound	Strand 5 — Earth and Universe
1. Weather	•													
2. Flight	•	•				•					•	•	•	
3. Sounds and music	•	•												
4. Water	•										•			
5. Falling	•								•		•	•		•
6. Light	•												•	
7. Don't throw it away	•			•	•	•			•		•			
8. Electricity and magnetism	•									•				
9. Food	•	•			•									
10. Senses	•	•						•			•			
11. Shapes and structures	•					•						•		
12. How things work	•					•				•	•	•		
13. Fibres	•					•								
14. Woodland life	•	•			•				•					
15. Growing and changing	•	•												
16. Time	•	•	•											•
17. Energy	•									•	•			
18. Measuring	• •					•						•	•	
19. How the Earth works	•	•		•	•				•		•			•
20. Starting and stopping	•	•									•	•		
21. Patterns and shapes	•		•				•	•						
22. The Earth in space	•								•		•			•
23. Science and design	• •		•									•		
24. Reproduction and heredity	•	•	•											
25. Computers and robots	•					•				•		•		
26. Waves and vibrations	•					•			•	•	•	•	•	
27. Don't waste energy	•			•		•			•	•	•	•		
28. Materials	•	•		•		•		•	•		•	•		
29. Presenting information	• •	•	•		•									

Contributory Authors
Brian Knapp, BSc, PhD and Peter Riley, BSc
Art Director
Duncan McCrae, BSc
Editor
Sarah George, BEd
Graphic illustrations
David Woodroffe
Print consultants
Landmark Production Consultants Ltd
Printed and bound in Hong Kong
Produced by
EARTHSCAPE EDITIONS

First published in the United Kingdom in 1993
by Atlantic Europe Publishing Company Limited,
86 Peppard Road, Sonning Common, Reading,
Berkshire, RG4 9RP, UK

Telephone 0734 723751; Fax 0734 724488

Copyright © 1993
Atlantic Europe Publishing Company Limited

The Atlantic Europe Publishing logo and circular cover device
are trademarks of Atlantic Europe Publishing Company Limited.

Publication Data
Knapp, Brian and Riley, Peter
  Reference guide to science in our world series –
  (Science in our world; 30)
  1. Teachers reference – For children
  I. Title   II. Series
500

ISBN 1-869860-28-4

Contents

Introduction

Science in our world is a series of 29 volumes, each a full 48 pages in extent, designed to enable the younger reader to develop a basic understanding of the principles and applications of science. The special introduction to each book is designed as a visual contents and to provide a rationale for the study about to be undertaken. The remainder of the book deals with the subject areas relevant to the National Curriculum in England and Wales and the Scottish Guidelines through the use of double page spreads.

Each spread is designed to be relatively independent of others in the book so that the reader can simply dip in. This is an unusual feature in a subject normally regarded as having a 'vertical structure' but it was thought to be important in a reference and study book for this age group.

Science in our world is designed to help young people find out about science; thus it is not so much fact-laden, as ideas-laden. Great emphasis is placed on the clarity of the page, with considerable white space left intentionally in order that the young reader will easily be able to progress around the page without feeling overburdened with captions or that they might have missed something.

Each spread is designed to have multiple reading levels: the introductory statement is in large type and sets the scene, the headed paragraphs contain the main lines of theory or application, while the smallest type of all is used to help add detail and explain features that might be complex or which have special names.

The books have many activities that can be done by children, often on their own, sometimes with the help of parents and teachers. The experiments are simple, reliable and use the minimum of equipment so they can mostly be done at home as well as in class. This gives the opportunity for parental involvement at this strategically important level of development.

The readers are invited to make models. These models have been designed by a teacher who works with younger pupils and who has ensured that each one is within the capability range of the target age group. The models are also designed to be visually appealing and to provide the child with an example whose standard of workmanship can be admired. This is why great attention is paid to the nature of the materials used in every case. This should also provide a guide to the quality and standards that parents and teachers can encourage their children to achieve.

The twenty nine books are intended to support the curriculum/guidelines and to provide teachers, pupils and parents with active support in all matters. In total, you can be confident that there is a substantial body of work to refer to: nearly 1400 pages, over 170,000 words, about 480 glossary items and more than 2000 index entries.

This Reference Guide is designed to help you get even more out of the *Science in our world* series by providing a quick reference to where essential topics may be found, what activities can be done on a particular topic, what materials will be needed and further references. There are also Work Cards that will enable children to work towards completing their attainment targets in a structured way.

The Work Cards are designed to be photocopiable – they are copyright free if used for educational purposes in the school – and can be organised in whatever way is appropriate. When photocopied and cut out they will make a ready file; multiple copies can be given out in class; and notes can be made on the back of them.

Finally there is a master glossary and index to the 29 volumes.

We hope that all the materials will help you in your important work, and we welcome further ideas and suggestions.

We hope you enjoy the series and find this book a valuable adjunct to your work.

Peter Riley/Brian Knapp, authors

For National Curriculum

The first 63 pages of this Reference Guide contain Work Cards. In this section of the book each of the twenty nine books in the series is allocated a double page spread. Each spread is divided into a Reference Card and three photocopiable Work Cards. On the Reference Card the pages selected for special study have been matched against the National Curriculum in the following way:

Where the page more directly relates to an Attainment Target (AT) and a Statement of Attainment (SoA) it is picked out in the table as:

AT/PoS	SoA/Key words
2	3

Where the page relates more directly to a Programme of Study (PoS) it is picked out as:

AT/PoS	SoA/Key words
2i	personal hygiene

The i figure indicates the appropriate paragraph in the Programme of Study and the key words help to locate the appropriate text in the paragraph.

For Scottish Guidelines

With a less heavily structured curriculum to follow, you will find that you will be able to skip the Attainment Target/Programme of Study section. Nevertheless, the subjects covered in the *Science in our world* series and the nature of the work material given in this reference guide have already been endorsed by many Scottish teachers as supporting their needs for the guidelines.

Photocopiable Reference Card and Work Cards

Each spread can be photocopied and the Reference Card and three Work Cards can then be cut out for use in the classroom.

This double page spread relates to one of the books in the *Science in our world* series.

This card gives you a rapid guide to the equipment you will need for activities on the Work Cards and tells you the assessments you will be covering. Photocopy this card and make a reference file for yourself.

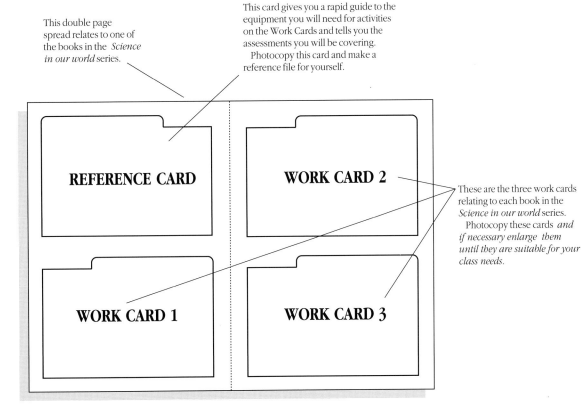

REFERENCE CARD

WORK CARD 2

WORK CARD 1

WORK CARD 3

These are the three work cards relating to each book in the *Science in our world* series. Photocopy these cards *and if necessary enlarge them until they are suitable for your class needs.*

WORK CARD 1			WORK CARD 2			WORK CARD 3		
Rising air			Water in the air			Clouds		
Page	*AT/PoS*	*SoA/Key words*	*Page*	*AT/PoS*	*SoA/Key words*	*Page*	*AT/PoS*	*SoA/Key words*
6-7	4v	motion of the Earth	14-17	3iv	water cycle	18-25	3iv	water cycle
8-13	3	4d	26-27	3	4d			
38-39	2	3b	30-33	3iv	water cycle			
42-43	3iv	weather observations						

Equipment
p.7 Globe or ball, torch , dark room
p.8 Bowl, water, food colouring
p.10 Alcohol in thread thermometer
p.13 Beaufort wind scale, compass

Assessment Activities
1. How does air temperature change in one place over a few days? (p.10)
2. Does air temperature in different parts of the environment change in the same way? (p.38)
3. Can you use a wind-sock to tell windspeed? Correlate the wind-sock movement with the Beaufort wind scale.

Equipment
p.14 Plastic bag, string, plant
p.15 Saucers, felt-tip pen, measuring cylinder
p.17 Four sticks, polythene sheet, string, stone, beaker
p.26 Coloured paper, pencil, water
p.27 Rain gauge

Assessment Activities
1. Does water evaporate at the same rate in different places? Set up several saucers. Put the same volume of water in each. Mark the level with a felt-tip pen and record the position of the water level every day for a few days.
2. Is there a relationship between the amount of rain, windspeed and direction, air temperature and cloud type?

Equipment
Show how 1. Large pieces of paper and pencils. (Optional - blue paper, cotton wool, white and grey paints)
Show how 2. A range of weather recording equipment

Assessment Activities
1. Can you see as far every day? Find the distance of local landmarks using a map. Use these landmarks to record how far you can clearly see. Look for changes during hot days and in periods of changeable weather.
2. How does the amount of cloud cover change? Divide the sky into eighths. A sky full of cloud is 8/8 or overcast. Record the cloud cover hourly or daily and correlate with other weather recordings.

WORK CARD **1**
SCIENCE IN OUR WORLD WORK CARDS
Rising air

❓ Find out from Book 1: Weather

The number shown like this (p.00) tells you which page to find the answer.

1. How does the air move in the atmospher e? (p.8)
2. What happens to the air in the tr opics? (p.8 and p.9)
3. What happens to the air over the desert? (p.9)
4. What can you see in the air in cooler r egions of the world? (p.9)
5 What air temperatur e is comfortable for most people? (p.10)

6. What is the dif ference between a br eeze and a wind? (p.12)
7. What dif ferences are there between a gale and a hurricane? (p.12)
8. How is city air dif ferent from country air? (p.38 and p.39)
9. How can air pr essure be measur ed? (p.43)
10. How does air pr essure affect the weather? (p.43)

✳ Show how . . .

1. a sunbeam can cover a small ar ea of the earth or a lar ge area. How does this af fect our weather?
2. swirling water moves. How does this help to explain the cloud patter ns that can be seen from space?

Find out more

Look at these other Science in our world books for more information.

Book	Page	Heading
Measuring	p.24	Air pressure
How the Earth works	p.32	The atmosphere

? Find out from Book 1: Weather

The number shown like this (p.00) tells you which page to find the answer.

1. Why can the water in the air not be seen? (p.14)
2. Where does most of the water in the air come from? (p.14)
3. How does the air feel if it has got a lot of water vapour in it? (p.14)
4. When does condensation form? (p.16)
5. How does dew form? (p.16)
6. Why does dew disappear? (p.17)
7. What is precipitation? (p.26)
8. Name five kinds of precipitation. (p.26)
9. How does frost form? (p.30)
10. How does a snowflake form? (p.32)

✳ Show how . . .

1. condensation may be collected from the air. Try the activity on p.17, then make a large drawing of it and put on arrows showing how water got from the air to the beaker
2. big raindrops can be (p.26)

❗ Find out more

Look at these other Science in our world books for more information.

Book	Page	Heading
Water	p.12	From rain to rivers
Falling	p.26	Falling water

© 1993 Atlantic Europe Publishing Co Ltd

? Find out from Book 1: Weather

The number shown like this (p.00) tells you which page to find the answer.

1. What is fog? (p.18)
2. Why can't you see in fog? (p.19)
3. What is mist? (p.19)
4. How do clouds form? (p.20)
5. What are cumulus clouds? Do they bring rain? (p.22)
6. What are stratus clouds? What kind of weather do they bring? (p.22)
7. What is a cumulonimbus cloud? What happens inside it? (p.23)
8. What are cirrus clouds? Do they bring rain? (p.23)
9. Which cloud patterns show rain? (p.24)
10. Which area is clear of cloud? (p.25)

✳ Show how . . .

1. clouds change during the day by drawing part of the sky every hour on a large piece of paper
2. clouds and weather change by keeping a daily record of the clouds, the air temperature, the amount of rain and wind

❗ Find out more

Look at these other Science in our world books for more information.

Book	Page	Heading
Water	p.8	Where water comes from
Light	p.6	Sunlight

© 1993 Atlantic Europe Publishing Co Ltd

WORK CARD 1			WORK CARD 2			WORK CARD 3		
Rising in the air			Powered flight			From air to space		
Page	*AT/PoS*	*SoA/Key words*	*Page*	*AT/PoS*	*SoA/Key words*	*Page*	*AT/PoS*	*SoA/Key words*
6-11,14-15	4	3c,4c	16-17	4	3c,4c	30-35	4iii	3c, 4c transport
			18-19	2i	animal movement	39	4i	control
			20-21	4	3c, 4c	40-45	4	3c, 4c
			22-23	2i	animal movement			
			28-29, 37	4	4c			

Equipment

p.6 and p.7 Two pieces of wood, string, a straw, a piece of stiff card, glue. (You may need several sets of this equipment for Assessment Activity 1). Hair dryer - optional

p.9 Tracing paper, thick aluminium foil, scissors, short stick, a pin or piece of thick fuse wire, a bead, a table lamp

Assessment Activities

1. How does the size of the curve affect the way the wing lifts? To make a fair test place each wing in turn a certain distance from a hair dryer.
2. Can the design of the aluminium foil detector be modified to see if a more sensitive detector can be made?

Equipment

p.17 Thin sheet of cardboard or plastic, scissors, sticky tape to hold the blades in place for younger pupils, a pin, a stick. Hair drier - optional

p.21 Piece of card, paper clip, scissors

p.21 Piece of cardboard, scissors, cotton reel, string, pencil, sticky tape to hold rotor to pencil

Assessment Activities

1. How does the shape and size of the blades affect the way the propeller spins? Each propeller could be tested with a hair dryer.
2. How does the size and shape of the rotors affect the way the autogyro falls?

Equipment

p.40 Two pieces of thin cardboard, paper clip, glue

p.12 Sheets of paper, stop clock, long tape measure, large room such as school hall

p.44 String, table-tennis ball, two small sticks, two pieces of cardboard, glue

Assessment Activities

1. How does the size of the hovercraft box or tube affect its lift?
2. How does the shape of the wings of a paper dart affect its speed?

Note:

All these activities can be made more relevant to AT4 3c and 4c if reference is made to the force of gravity opposing the forces that make flight possible.

? Find out from Book 2: Flight

The number shown like this (p.00) tells you which page to find the answer.

1. How does flying happen? (p.6)
2. Which way does hot air move? (p.8)
3. How is hot air made for a balloon? (p.8)
4. Why must a hot-air balloon be the size of a house? (p.8)
5. Why does a kite need good wind to fly? (p.10)
6. What happens to the air as the wind rushes past the kite? (p.10)
7. How is the kite lifted in the air? (p.10)
8. How does a pilot get a hang-glider into the air? (p.11)
9. How is a glider launched into the air? (p.14)
10. What do glider pilots use to keep their glider flying? (p.15)

✳ Show how . . .

1. the shape of the wings helps it rise in the air (p.6 and p.7)
2. you can detect hot air in the classr oom (p.9)

! Find out more

Look at these other Science in our world books for more information.

Book	Page Heading
Falling	p.28 Falling gently
Measuring	p.18 Weight

? Find out from **Book 2: Flight**

The number shown like this (p.00) tells you which page to find the answer.

1. What happens when a propeller turns? (p.1)
2. How does an insect make its wings go up and down? (p.19)
3. How do an insect's wings get it off the ground? (p.19)
4. What are the jobs of a helicopter's rotor? (p.20)
5. What is the tail rotor of a helicopter for? (p.20)
6. How can a helicopter be landed safely if its engine fails? (p.21)
7. How does a bird use its outer and inner wing for flight? (p.22 and p.23)
8. How do birds and insects control their flight? (p.28)
9. How can an aeroplane be made to turn, dive and climb? (p.28 and p.29)
10. How does a jet engine work? (p.37)

✳ Show how . . .

1. you can make a propeller that turns when you blow it (p.17)
2. the autogyro effect works on a piece of card and paper clip (p.21)
3. a model helicopter can lift into the air (p.21)

! Find out more

Look at these other Science in our world *books for more information.*

Book	Page	Heading
Energy	p.24	Why we use stored energy
Starting and Stopping	p.30	Changing speed in the air

© 1993 Atlantic Europe Publishing Co Ltd

? Find out from **Book 2: Flight**

The number shown like this (p.00) tells you which page to find the answer.

1. Why can't people fly? (p.30)
2. How can you make an aeroplane that you can fly with your own muscle power? (p.31)
3. What did the Wright brothers do? (p.32 and p.33)
4. What are biplanes and monoplanes? (p.33)
5. What do aeroplanes need to make them travel very fast? (p.34)
6. What is an autopilot? (p.39)
7. What lifts the Space Shuttle? (p.42)
8. Why can space stations have clumsy-looking shapes? (p.43)
9. What are satellites used for? (p.44)

✳ Show how . . .

1. a hovercraft works (p.40)
2. fast a paper dart can fly (p.12)
3. a satellite travels around the Earth (p.44)

! Find out more

Look at these other Science in our world *books for more information.*

Book	Page	Heading
Falling	p.44	Living without gravity
Energy	p.16	Electricity from the sun

© 1993 Atlantic Europe Publishing Co Ltd

WORK CARD 1			WORK CARD 2			WORK CARD 3		
Sounds and how you hear them			Rhythm			Strings and wind		
Page	*AT/PoS*	*SoA/Key words*	*Page*	*AT/PoS*	*SoA/Key words*	*Page*	*AT/PoS*	*SoA/Key words*
6-7	4	5f	25-29	4iv	vibrating objects	30-39	4iv	vibrating objects
10-11	2i	behaviour						
12-13	4	5f						
14-15	2	5a (part)						
16-17	2i	health						

WORK CARD 1

Equipment

p.6 and p.7 Two paper cups, nail, string
p.15 Paper, sticky tape, scissors

Assessment Activities

1. How is the conduction of sound on the bush telephone affected by (a) the type of thread between the cups, (b) the length of the string? (p.6)
2. Does a cardboard ear funnel help you hear more clearly? How does the (a) diameter of the funnel rim, (b) length of the funnel and (c) direction of the funnel affect hearing?

WORK CARD 2

Equipment

p.27 Pieces of wood cut to different lengths, hard floor
p.17 Eight clean, empty bottles, measuring jug, water

Assessment Activity

1. How does the diameter and length of a drum affect its sound? Use thin card to make a range of tubes of different diameters and lengths. Cover one end of each tube with cling film. Make the film as tight as possible. Tap each 'drum' with a pencil.

WORK CARD 3

Equipment

p.32 Selection of clean, empty bottles without cracked or broken lips, piano
p.34 Scissors, plastic straw

Assessment Activity

1. How does the length of a vibrating elastic band affect its sound? Put an elastic band over a 15 cm long piece of wood. Place the end of a pencil between the band and the wood. Move the pencil to one end. Pluck the band. Press on the band with a finger tip at different distances from the pencil and pluck each time.

Extension

How does the thickness of the band affect the sound? (Safety glasses should be worn.)

 WORK CARD 1

SCIENCE IN OUR WORLD WORK CARDS
Sounds and how you hear them

? Find out from Book 3: Sounds and Music

The number shown like this (p.00) tells you which page to find the answer.

1. What produces sounds? (p.6)
2. Make a list of warning sounds. (p.10)
3. What does how much sound you hear depend on? (p.12)
4. Why is a knock on a door louder than a knock on a ruler? (p.12)
5. How does a loudspeaker work? (p.13)

6. What does the outer ear do? (p.15)
7. What do the ear bones do? (p.15)
8. What happens in the inner ear? (p.15)
9. What unit is the loudness of sound measured in? (p.17)
10. Give some examples of the loudness of different things. (p.17)

✳ Show how . . .

1. your voice can send vibrations down a string (p.6)
2. a funnel at your ear changes your hearing (p.15)

! Find out more

Look at these other Science in our world *books for more information.*

Book	Page	Heading
Senses	p.24	The range of sounds
Electricity and Magnetism	p.40	The speaking magnet

? Find out from **Book 3: Sounds and Music**

The number shown like this (p.00) tells you which page to find the answer.

1. What is a beat? (p.25 and p.46)
2. What is a rhythm? (p.27 and p.47)
3. What do you do to play a percussion instrument? (p.26)
4. How is a xylophone made? (p.26)
5. What are percussion instruments used for? (p.28 and p.47)

6. How is a tambourine played? (p.28)
7. What are maracas? (p.28)
8. Why does a base drum make a deeper sound than other drums? (p.29)
9. What makes a snare drum rattle? (p.29)
10. Which players in a pop band give the music extra rhythm? (p.43)

✳ Show how . . .

1. you can make different rhythms by clapping your hands (p.25)
2. you can arrange pieces of wood in a musical scale (p.27)
3. you can play a tune by striking bottles filled with different amounts of water (p.27)

! Find out more

Look at these other Science in our world books for more information.

Book	Page	Heading
Time	p.20	The pendulum
How things work	p.38	Bells, buzzers and chimes
Waves and Vibrations	p.19	Matching waves and beats

© 1993 ATLANTIC EUROPE PUBLISHING CO LTD

? Find out from **Book 3: Sounds and Music**

The number shown like this (p.00) tells you which page to find the answer.

1. What happens to make a sound when a piano key is pressed? (p.30)
2. How do the strings produce a sound in a lute, a harp and a harpsichord? (p.31)
3. What makes the notes in trumpets, recorders and organs? (p.32)
4. What is the slot at the top of a recorder used for? (p.32)

5. What happens when you put your fingers over the holes of a recorder? (p.32)
6. What is a reed and what sort of sound does it make? (p.34)
7. Can you name three instruments which have reeds? (p.34)
8. Name three brass instruments. (p.36)
9. What do valves do? (p.37 and p.47)

✳ Show how . . .

1. bottles can be made to give a musical note by blowing across them. Can any notes be matched to those on a piano? (p.32)
2. you can make a reed that works (p.34)

! Find out more

Look at these other Science in our world books for more information.

Book	Page	Heading
Shapes and Structures	p.24	Tight wires
Measuring	p.20	Sensitive measurement

© 1993 ATLANTIC EUROPE PUBLISHING CO LTD

WORK CARD 1			WORK CARD 2			WORK CARD 3		
Water on the move			**Properties of water**			**Using water**		
Page	*AT/PoS*	*SoA/Key words*	*Page*	*AT/PoS*	*SoA/Key words*	*Page*	*AT/PoS*	*SoA/Key words*
8-9	3iv	water cycle	6-7,28	3i	solid, liquid, gas	20	3i	filtering
14-15	3	4e	37	3i	solubility	22	4	3c
18-19	4	4b	38	4	4c	24-27	2	3b
42-43	4ii	renewable energy	40	4ii	heating and cooling	29-31	4	4c
			45	4ii	heat	42	4	5b
						44	4	4b

Equipment

p.10 Glass, straw, piece of Plasticine or Blu-tack, pen, ruler, salt, spoon
p.13 Tray, sand, wooden block for tray support, water supply
p.19 Stiff card, pair of compasses, pencil, scissors, knitting needle, bead, water tap

Assessment Activities

1. Do soils from different places have the same layers of sediments? Stir each soil in turn in a glass of water and measure the bands of sediment with a ruler. (p.15)
2. Try various waterwheel designs. Fit each design to a knitting needle so both can turn together. Add a Plasticine weight on a string and see how quickly the wheel can raise the weight. (p.19)

Equipment

p.28 Ice cube, glass of water, ruler
p.37 Cold cooking oil, water, glass, spoon, washing-up liquid
p.38 Glass of clean water, kitchen towel, clean paper clip, washing-up liquid
p.40 Very cold water, cork with clear plastic straw through it, bottle, bowl of hot water

Assessment Activity

1. Which washing-up liquid disperses oil the best? A measuring cylinder is needed to measure out volumes of water, oil and washing-up liquid. A clock may be needed to time the amount of stirring. (p.37)

Equipment

p.22 Clear plastic tubes, funnel, jug of water, bucket or sink
p.30 Clear tank, bottle, water
p.31 Clear tank, water, Plasticine, spoon

Assessment Activities

1. How does the funnel height affect the water speed? Investigate with a ruler and a stopclock. (p.23)
2. How much water is used by a class at break or lunchtime? This could be worked out by careful organisation and measuring by the pupils. (p.24)

 WORK CARD 1

SCIENCE IN OUR WORLD WORK CARDS
Water on the move

? Find out from **Book 4: Water**

The number shown like this (p.00) tells you which page to find the answer.

1. How does water get from the oceans to the rivers? (p.8 and p.9)
2. How much of the world's water is made up of sea water? (p.10)
3. Why is it harder to sink in sea water than swimming pool water? (p.11)
4. What do rivers do to the land? (p.13)
5. Why do fast flowing rivers carry away large objects? (p.14)
6. Why are river pebbles smooth? (p.14)
7. How is a river's power used by a water wheel? (p.18)
8. What are the water wheels in a power station called? (p.19)
9. What do oceans carry? (p.42)
10. Why don't rivers freeze quickly in cold weather? (p.43)

✳ Show how . . .

1. a floating object behaves in water when salt is added (p.10)
2. soil behaves like a sponge (p.12)
3. rivers can shape the land (p.13)

Find out more

Look at these other Science in our world books for more information.

Book	Page	Heading
Weather	p.26	Rain and hail
How the Earth works	p.40	Plants

? Find out from Book 4: Water

The number shown like this (p.00) tells you which page to find the answer.

1. What are the three forms of water? (p.6)
2. What temperature is the melting point of water? What happens to water when this point is reached? (p.7)
3. What is the boiling point of water? What happens to the water when this point is reached? (p.7)
4. Why does ice float in water? (p.28)
5. How much of an iceberg can be seen above the water? (p.28)
6. Which substances do not mix with water? (p.36)
7. What special chemicals help these substances to mix? (p.36)
8. What happens to water when it warms up and cools down? (p.40)
9. What is unusual about water when it freezes? (p.40)

✱ Show how . . .

1. much ice is below the water when a cube floats (p.28)
2. to float a paper clip on water and then sink it without touching it. Try to explain what happens.

! Find out more

Look at these other Science in our world books for more information.

Book	Page	Heading
How things work	p.20	Sprays and jets
Measuring	p.12	Volume

? Find out from Book 4: Water

The number shown like this (p.00) tells you which page to find the answer.

1. What could be in water to harm us? (p.20)
2. What are the places called where water is cleaned? (p.21)
3. Describe what the water pipes under a big city are like. (p.22)
4. How much tap water can do we use in a day? (p.24)
5. How do farmers use river water for their crops? (p.27)
6. How can water help to move logs? (p.29)
7. What does water do when you push a bottle into it? (p.30)
8. What balances the weight of a ship in the ocean? (p.31)
9. How is water used in solar heating? (p.42)
10. Where does the steam do its work on a steam engine? (p.44)

✱ Show how . . .

1. the height of a funnel of water affects the speed of the water running into a bucket (p.23)
2. to float a spoon on water (p.31)

! Find out more

Look at these other Science in our world books for more information.

Book	Page	Heading
Food	p.45	What's in a drink
Time	p.16	Old timekeepers

WORK CARD 1			WORK CARD 2			WORK CARD 3		
Gravity and space			**Gravity and fun**			**Gravity and work**		
Page	*AT/PoS*	*SoA/Key words*	*Page*	*AT/PoS*	*SoA/Key words*	*Page*	*AT/PoS*	*SoA/Key words*
6-7,11	4 4iii	3c forces	8-9,12-13,			10-11,14-15,		
40-41	4v	sun and planets	18-19,22-23,			16-17	4 4iii	3c forces
42,44-45	4iii	3c forces	34-39	4 4iii	3c forces	20-21,		
						27-28	3l 2iii	plants suiting habitat
						35	4	4c

WORK CARD 1 — Equipment
p.7 Marble, feather, ruler, stop clock
p.11 Bowl, flour, marble

Assessment Activity
1. Can a model moonscape be made by dropping small pieces of gravel into soft plaster of Paris? Use a circular aluminium foil dish and pour a plaster of Paris/water mixture into it. Drop pieces of aquarium gravel into it one at a time to make craters. Safety spectacles should be worn. Extension - what is the effect of altering the ratio of plaster of Paris powder to water?

WORK CARD 2 — Equipment
p.12 Selection of balls made from different materials
p.23 Pile of sand and a ball
p.38 Table tennis ball, thread

Assessment Activities
1. Does the length of a pendulum affect the way it swings? Use different lengths of string and a stop clock. (p.19)
2. Does the mass of a pendulum affect the way it swings? Use different masses of Plasticine and a stop clock.
3. How does the amount of liquid in a bottle affect the ease with which it is tipped over? Use a plastic bottle, measuring jug, short plank, ruler, wooden blocks (to put under one end of the plank).

WORK CARD 3 — Equipment
p.10 Deep sand tray, wooden rod, plastic cup with wire support, string, wooden support, cotton reel, nail
p.14 Triangle of wood, ruler, objects
p.16 Measuring jug, two plastic cups with wire supports, string, two cotton reels, two nails, wooden supports, water, sand
p.20 Wooden support with hook, elastic band, hook and pointer made from stiff wire, string, shallow tray, sticky tape to hold string to tray, cardboard strip.

Assessment Activity
Which design is best for a slow-falling parachute? (p.29)

? Find out from Book 5: Falling (Gravity)

The number shown like this (p.00) tells you which page to find the answer.

1. Who first explained gravity? (p.6)
2. What does gravity do? (p.6)
3. How would the weight of a kilo of apples change if you took them to the moon? (p.7)
4. How is our Solar System held together? (p.40)
5. What does the Sun's gravity do? (p.41)
6. What do planets trap with their gravity? (p.41)
7. How is a shooting star formed? (p.42)
8. What would happen if there was no gravity? (p.44)
9. How do astronauts move about outside their spacecraft? (p.45)
10. How would a meal in space be different from one on Earth? (p.45)

✳ Show how . . .

1. a marble and a feather fall and explain what you see (p.6)
2. your weight would change if you went to the moon (p.7)
3. a meteorite makes a crater and explain what can be seen when this happens (p.11)

❗ Find out more

Look at these other Science in our world *books for more information.*

Book	Page	Heading
How the Earth works	p.8	How the Earth is formed
The Earth and space	p.22	The Earth's tides

? Find out from **Book 5: Falling (Gravity)**

The number shown like this (p.00) tells you which page to find the answer.

1. What happens to you when you ride a roller coaster? (p.8)
2. What is the size of the G-force that people feel on a large corkscrew ride? (p.9)
3. What happens when something falls to the ground? (p.12)
4. How does a hopper and a trampoline work? (p.13)
5. What is a pendulum? (p.18)
6. When does gravity make a swing move faster rather than slow it down? (p.19)
7. Why don't you hit the water hard when you come down a water-slide? (p.22)
8. Why are some children's toys difficult to knock over? (p.34)
9. How does gravity affect the way that you throw things? (p.36)
10. What happens to you as you spin on a fairground roundabout? (p.38)

✱ Show how . . .

1. you can compare the 'bounciness' of balls and explain why they bounce (p.12)
2. a ramp or slope makes falling safer (p.23)

! Find out more

Look at these other Science in our world books for more information.

Book	Page	Heading
Time	p.22	Clocks with pendulums
Starting and Stopping	p.8	Falling weight mover

© 1993 ATLANTIC EUROPE PUBLISHING CO LTD

? Find out from **Book 5: Falling (Gravity)**

The number shown like this (p.00) tells you which page to find the answer.

1. How does gravity help in pile-driving and wood-cutting? (p.10 and p.11)
2. Write about three ways that gravity and balancing can help us. (p.14 and p.15)
3. How does gravity work in a stretch balance? (p.20)
4. Where are stretch balances particularly useful? (p.21)
5. How does gravity turn a water-wheel? (p.27)
6. How does hydro-electric power help the environment? (p.27)
7. What is another name for air resistance? (p.28)
8. What makes some buildings more stable than others? (p.35)
9. How are cars designed to stop them rolling over on a bend? (p.35)

✱ Show how . . .

1. you can balance objects of different weights (p.14)
2. you can use gravity to lift things (p.16)

! Find out more

Look at these other Science in our world books for more information.

Book	Page	Heading
Shapes and Structures	p.14	Arches
How things work	p.18	Scales

© 1993 ATLANTIC EUROPE PUBLISHING CO LTD

SCIENCE IN OUR WORLD WORK CARDS

REFERENCE CARD

Book 6: Light

WORK CARD 1			WORK CARD 2			WORK CARD 3		
Reflections			**Light on the move**			**Colour and shadows**		
Page	*AT/PoS*	*SoA/Key words*	*Page*	*AT/PoS*	*SoA/Key words*	*Page*	*AT/PoS*	*SoA/Key words*
12-21, 24	4	3d,5e	6,8-9, 22, 26-27	4iv	light through objects	7	4iv	light varies in colour
			28-29	2	5a(part)	34	4iv	light through water
						40	4iv	colour filter
						42-43	4/4v	2d sundial
						44	4/4iv	2d shadows

WORK CARD 1

Equipment

p.12 Table lamp, white paper, object
p.14 Bicycle reflector
p.16 Flat mirror

Assessment Activity

1. How does the angle of the ray striking a mirror compare with the angle of the reflected ray? Use a torch and comb to make a ray like those on p.27. Turn the mirror so the ray strikes it obliquely. Draw a line outwards from the mirror at right angles to its surface and use a protractor to measure the angle the incident and reflected ray make with this line. Move the mirror by stages until it almost faces the ray striking it and measure the angles at each stage.

WORK CARD 2

Equipment

p.8 Candle, wide-necked jar, dark room
p.11 Torch
p.23 Wood, long pins, small flat sided tank of water
p.27 Comb, cardboard, torch, selection of lenses made from glasses and bottles

Assessment Activity

1. How does the curve of the glass affect the way the light rays go after passing through the glass? Use the equipment on p.27 and a collection of lenses and curved glass to try and relate the curvature of the lenses to the distance the rays travel to their focal point after passing through the lens.

WORK CARD 3

Equipment

p.7 Glass tank or globe of water, torch, disinfectant which goes milky in water, white paper, dark room
p.36 Piece of card, sharp pencil, coloured pencils
p.43 Stick, area of flat ground in sunny position, small stones

Assessment Activities

1. How does the height of a torch affect the shadow of an object it is shining on? Use a block, white paper, pencil and rulers to find out
2. How does the shadow change with the distance from the torch?

WORK CARD 1

SCIENCE IN OUR WORLD WORK CARDS

Reflection

? Find out from **Book 6: Light**

The number shown like this (p.00) tells you which page to find the answer.

1. Which objects reflect light and which do not? (p.12)
2. Why can you see the moon? (p.14)
3. Why do clouds look dark grey? (p.15)
4. Why do mirrors give a clear picture? (p.16)
5. What is another name for a reflection? (p.17)

6. Make a drawing of a periscope and show with a line how light passes through it. (p.19)
7. What are convex mirrors and where would you find them? (p.21 and p.46)
8. What are concave mirrors and where would you find them? (p.21 and p.46)
9. What makes a crystal sparkle? (p.24)

✳ Show how . . .

1. white paper can be used as a reflector (p.12)
2. many reflecting surfaces are on a bicycle reflector (p.14)
3. you can make a secret message that can only be read with a mirror (p.16)

! Find out more

Look at these other Science in our world books for more information.

Book	Page	Heading
Sounds and Music	p.18	Room for echoes
How things work	p.24	Binoculars

WORK CARD 2

Light on the move

? Find out from Book 6: Light

The number shown like this (p.00) tells you which page to find the answer.

1. How does light travel? (p.6)
2. How is a fluorescent tube different from a light bulb? (p.8 and p.9)
3. How can sailors tell one lighthouse from another? (p.10)
4. When does light change direction? (p.22)
5. Why does a mirage appear? (p.23)
6. What is a lens? (p.26 and p.46)
7. How do things appear through a lens with a concave surface? (p.26 and p.46)
8. How do things appear through a lens with a convex surface? (p.26 and p.46)
9. How does the lens in the eye change to help us see? (p.28)
10. What lens can be added to the eyes to help some people see more clearly? (p.28)

✳ Show how . . .

1. you could use light to send messages (p.11)
2. light travels through a glass of water and explain why (p.27)

! Find out more

Look at these other Science in our world books for more information.

Book	Page	Heading
How things work	p.34	Lamps
Senses	p.28	Seeing the light
Presenting information	p.24	Understanding eyesight problems

WORK CARD 3

Colour and Shadows

? Find out from Book 6: Light

The number shown like this (p.00) tells you which page to find the answer.

1. What colours are produced from the white light of sunlight? (p.7)
2. What are rainbows and when are you able to see them? (p.34)
3. What is a spectrum? (p.34 and p.47)
4. How many colours are in the visible spectrum and what are their names? (p.36)
5. What is a filter and how does it work? (p.40)
6. How is a shadow made? (p.42)
7. What is the difference between an eclipse of the sun and an eclipse of the moon? (p.42)
8. What must you use to tell the time with a shadow? (p.43)
9. What is an opaque object? (p.44 and p.47)
10. How does the size of a shadow change? (p.44)

✳ Show how . . .

1. the light changes as it passes through a model 'atmosphere' and explain what you see (p.7)
2. you can make white light from different colours and explain what you see (p.36)

! Find out more

Look at these other Science in our world books for more information.

Book	Page	Heading
Senses	p.36	Seeing beyond the rainbow
Fibres	p.38	Dyes and colour

WORK CARD 1			WORK CARD 2			WORK CARD 3		
Getting rid of rubbish			**Recycling**			**Paper and wood**		
Page	*AT/PoS*	*SoA/Key words*	*Page*	*AT/PoS*	*SoA/Key words*	*Page*	*AT/PoS*	*SoA/Key words*
10	2iii	human activity	6-7	2iii	human activity	36	3i	grouping materials
12	2iii	human activity	20	3	5a			
14	4	4c	23	3iii	origins of materials	8-9	3ii	3a
16-19	2iii	human activity	30	2iii	human activity	22	3	origins of materials
41	4	3b	32-33,			24	3ii	3a
44-45	2iv	waste disposal	35,37	3iii	origins of materials	38	3	origins of materials
			42	2	5d	39	3ii	3a origins of materials

Equipment
p.10 Protective gloves and a plastic bag per person
p.12 Cardboard or bucket, paper, sticky tape, wallpaper paste

Assessment Activities
1. Which surfaces are easiest to clean with a brush and water? Make a small area of each different surface dirty with chewing gum, food remains, oil, etc. and work out a fair test to compare their ease of cleaning.
2. What amounts of different rubbish do people in the class/school get rid of at school during the course of a day/week?

Equipment
p.20 . Hair drier, garden sieve, magnet, bowl of water
p.43. Selection of foods, plastic bags and ties or rubber bands, a safe place to put the bags while the contents are decomposing

Assessment Activities
1. Which materials in rubbish break down in the soil? Work out a fair test. The materials should be left in the soil for a few months.
2. Find out which food material decays fastest in its raw state when enclosed in a clear plastic bag and not opened again.

Equipment
p.9 Goods in paper or cardboard wrappers
p.24. Two square frames, old net curtain, nails, glue, bowl of water, whisk or fork, white paper, kitchen towel

Assessment Activity
1. How do the strengths of different papers vary? Test each paper by pinning it to a wooden bar and adding weights to an attached scale pan until the paper tears.

 **WORK CARD 1** SCIENCE IN OUR WORLD WORK CARDS
Getting rid of rubbish

? Find out from Book 7: Don't throw it away

The number shown like this (p.00) tells you which page to find the answer.

1. What is litter and where can it build up quickly? (p.10)
2. What should you use if you go litter-picking? (p.10)
3. What are important features of a litter bin? (p.12)
4. What do car tyres, shoes and Nature leave on the streets? (p.14)
5. How does a street-cleaning machine work? (p.14)
6. Why is it important to deal with rubbish as soon as possible? (p.17)
7. Where is rubbish dumped and what is a rubbish dump called? (p.16 and p.17)
8. How do people who are short of money use rubbish? (p.18 and p.19)
9. How can heat from rubbish be put to good use? (p.41)
10. How can the wastes of animals and plants be useful? (p.44 and p.45)

✳ Show how . . .

1. you think a poster about litter for your town may help the litter problem (p.11)
2. you can make a safe children's toy from litter (p.19)

! Find out more

Look at these other Science in our world books for more information.

Book	Page	Heading
Woodland life	p.34	A lot of rot
Energy	p.34	Choosing a fuel

? Find out from **Book 7: Don't throw it away**

The number shown like this (p.00) tells you which page to find the answer.

1. Why do we throw things away when they go wrong? (p.6)
2. What are disposables? (p.7 and p.46)
3. What is the secret of good sorting and why is it important? (p.20)
4. What materials can be taken to a recycling centre? (p.23)
5. What happens at a scrap yard? (p.30)
6. What metals are used to make food cans and drink cans? (p.32)
7. Why is it useful to make new cans from old cans? (p.33)
8. How can we improve the environment by recycling glass? (p.35)
9. How are old building materials recycled? (p.37)
10. How can dead plants be recycled so that they can be used in the garden? (p.42)

✳ Show how . . .

1. sieving a pile of rubbish helps sort the rubbish out (p.20)
2. using a magnet on small rubbish items like pencil shavings and paperclips helps sort out the rubbish

! Find out more

Look at these other Science in our world *books for more information.*

Book	Page	Heading
How the Earth works	p.38	Soil
Materials	p.44	Materials and the environment

? Find out from **Book 7: Don't throw it away**

The number shown like this (p.00) tells you which page to find the answer.

1. Make a table or chart showing the amounts of different rubbish in a typical rubbish bin. (p.6)
2. Why are wrappings large and colourful? (p.6)
3. What is another name for wrappers? (p.8)
4. Why is packaging important? (p.9)
5. Why should you sort paper and cardboard? (p.9)
6. How should paper be sorted? (p.22)
7. What gives paper its strength? (p.24)
8. What is chipboard? (p.38)
9. How can tree bark be used? (p.39)
10. What are hardwoods? Why is it important to re-use them? (p.39 and p.46)

✳ Show how . . .

1. much packaging there is in a few common items bought by your family (p.9)
2. you can make recycled paper (p.24)

! Find out more

Look at these other Science in our world *books for more information.*

Book	Page	Heading
Fibres	p.20	Secrets of paper
Shapes and Structures	p.12	Crinkles

WORK CARD 1
Magnetism

Page	AT/PoS	SoA/Key words
28	4	2a
30	4i	magnetic material
32	4i	simple circuits
34-35	4i	magnetic material
40-41	4iv	vibrating objects

Equipment
p.28 Magnet, iron nail
p.29 Screw driver, magnet
p.30 Shallow dish, water, polystyrene float, needle, magnet
p.31 Iron filings, card, magnet
p.33 Large steel nail, battery, doorbell switch, tube, five metres of insulated copper wire.

Assessment Activities
1. How can you measure the strength of different magnets? Make a collection of magnets and use panel pins or paper clips to find out.
2. How does the length of wire in a coil affect the strength of the electromagnet? (See p.33 for circuit.)

WORK CARD 2
Basic electricity

Page	AT/PoS	SoA/Key words
6,8,11-12	4i	flow of electricity
24-25	4	5b

Equipment
p.7 Battery, two wires, bulb
p.8 Plastic comb
p.24 Lemon, knife, zinc and copper strips

Assessment Activities
1. Which everyday items can build up static electricity? Rub a selection of items and test with pieces of squared paper. (p.9)
2. Do materials behave in different ways when they are charged? Rub a piece of perspex (positive charge) and hang it on a thread. Rub a piece of polythene (negative charge) and bring it near to the perspex. Repeat with two pieces of perspex and polythene. Try with other plastics.

WORK CARD 3
In the circuit

Page	AT/PoS	SoA/Key words
14	4i	mains electricity
16-17	4i	heating
18-21	4	3a
22	4ii	energy transfer
26-27	4i	different components
36	4i	magnetic effects

Equipment
p.18 and p.21 Battery, wires, bulb, switch
p.37 Metal cake tin, strong salt solution, barrel magnet, one long and one short piece of stiff copper wire, wire support, battery and two wires.

Assessment Activities
1. Which everyday items are conductors or insulators? (p.13)
2. Does the length of a conductor affect its resistance? Using the carbon from a split pencil find out how the length of it in the circuit affects the brightness of the bulb.

 WORK CARD 1

SCIENCE IN OUR WORLD WORK CARDS
Magnetism

? Find out from Book 8: Electricity and Magnetism

The number shown like this (p.00) tells you which page to find the answer.

1. What is a magnet? (p.28)
2. What is a pole and how many poles has a magnet got? (p.28)
3. What is magnetic rock called? (p.29)
4. Why does the Earth act like a giant bar magnet? (p.30)
5. What sort of magnet can you switch on and off? (p.32)
6. How does an electromagnet help to move scrap metal? (p.32)
7. How does a cassette tape work? (p.34)
8. What is a floppy disk and what is it used for? (p.34)
9. Where is there an electromagnet in a telephone and what does it do? (p.40 and 41)

✳ Show how . . .

1. you can make a magnet from a screwdriver and then perform some tests with it (p.29)
2. make a compass and point to places north, south, east and west

❗ Find out more

Look at these other Science in our world *books for more information.*

Book	Page	Heading
How things work	p.38	Bells, buzzers and chimes
How the Earth works	p.10	Inside the Earth

? Find out from **Book 8: Electricity and Magnetism**

The number shown like this (p.00) tells you which page to find the answer.

1. What controls the flow of electricity through a wire? (p.6)
2. What is the pressure on the flow of electricity called? (p.6)
3. What is the flow of electricity called? (p.6)
4. What is static electricity? (p.8)
5. How does a spark occur? (p.8)
6. What is lightning? (p.11)
7. What is the difference between a conductor and an insulator? (p.12)
8. Name one conductor and three insulators. (p.12)
9. What is a solar cell? (p.24)
10. What is a battery made from? (p.25)

✳ Show how . . .

1. you can make electricity using a plastic comb (p.8)
2. you an make a battery from a lemon (p.24)

! Find out more

Look at these other Science in our world *books for more information.*

Book	Page	Heading
Weather	p.28	Thunder and lightning
Materials	p.22	Electrical conduction

© 1993 Atlantic Europe Publishing Co Ltd

? Find out from **Book 8: Electricity and Magnetism**

The number shown like this (p.00) tells you which page to find the answer.

1. What are trunk cables and how are they different from cables in the home? (p.14)
2. What happens if a lot of electricity goes through a cable? (p.16)
3. What is a fuse and how does it work? (p.17)
4. How are bulbs connected in series? (p.18)
5. How are mains sockets connected together? (p.20)
6. What is a parallel circuit? (p.21)
7. How is electric energy measured? (p.22)
8. How much energy does (a) a fluorescent tube, (b) a light bulb, (c) a kettle and (d) a stove use? (p.22)
9. How is electricity made in a power station and how does an electric motor work? (p.36)

✳ Show how . . .

1. to make a series and a parallel circuit and show what happens when a bulb is removed from each circuit. Explain what you see (p.18 and p.21)
2. an electric motor works (p.37)

! Find out more

Look at these other Science in our world *books for more information.*

Book	Page	Heading
Sounds and Music	p.42	Electrifying sounds
How Things Work	p.44	Heaters

© 1993 Atlantic Europe Publishing Co Ltd

WORK CARD 1			WORK CARD 2			WORK CARD 3		
What's in food			**The path of food**			**Food processing**		
Page	*AT/PoS*	*SoA/Key words*	*Page*	*AT/PoS*	*SoA/Key words*	*Page*	*AT/PoS*	*SoA/Key words*
9	2	4d	6-7	2	3a(part)	14-15	2i	safe handling
16-26	2i	Feeding, diet	10	2i	feeding	19,23	2i	diet
			12-13	2	4a(part)	32-35,		
						38,43	2i	safe handling
						41	2i	microbes

Equipment

p.20 Fatty foods and non-fatty foods, bowl of water, paper

Assessment Activity

1. Can the amount of energy in food be measured? Set fire to different nuts in a candle flame and time how long each one burns. The candle must be in a sand tray. Safety glasses must be worn and the nut must be on a long wire and held in a gloved hand.

Equipment

p.11 Stethoscope

Assessment Activities

1. How much food do slugs eat? The pupils will need a tank, moist compost, slugs, cabbage leaves, weighing scales. They will need to work out a plan which involves weighing food at daily intervals.
2. Do slugs have food preferences? Try them with a range of vegetable foods and record the results.

Equipment

p.14 Iodine from a chemist's shop (see Activity 1 below), plastic rod
p.30 Measuring jug, balance, water, towel

Assessment Activities

1. Which foods contain starch? Make a collection of food and put a drop of iodine on each one by dipping the rod in the bottle then carefully dabbing the food. Clean the rod between each dab. A blue-black colour shows the food contains starch. (p.14)
2. How much water do dry beans absorb when they are soaked before cooking?

WORK CARD 1

SCIENCE IN OUR WORLD WORK CARDS
What's in food?

? Find out from Book 9: Food

The number shown like this (p.00) tells you which page to find the answer.

1. What do each of the the meals from Africa, South America, Europe and SE Asia provide for the body? (p.9)
2. Which substances help our bodies to grow and in which foods do you find them? (p.16 and p.17)
3. What are carbohydrates and in which foods can you find them? (p.18, p.19 and p.46)
4. Why can too much fat be dangerous to older people? (p.21)

5. What are vitamins and in which foods do you find them? (p.22 and p.23)
6. Why do you need minerals? Name some examples of minerals. (p.24 and p.25)
7. Why is too much salt bad for people? (p.24)
8. Which foods are rich in fibre? What does fibre do? (p.26)

✳ Show how . . .

1. some foods contain fat by smearing them on paper and holding the paper up to the light. If you can see light through the paper, the food contains fat (p.20)

! Find out more

Look at these other Science in our world books for more information.

Book	Page	Heading
How the Earth works	p.38	Soil
Water	p.20	Clear but not clean

? Find out from **Book 9: Food**

The number shown like this (p.00) tells you which page to find the answer.

1. Where do plants get their energy from? (p.6)
2. What animals are herbivores and what can they digest? (p.6)
3. What types of food can we digest? (p.6)
4. What is a food chain? (p.6)
5. Why do we need to eat a variety of foods? (p.7)
6. What is saliva? (p.10)
7. What do your teeth do to food? (p.13)
8. How long does the food stay in the stomach. What liquid does it mix with there? (p.13)
9. What happens to the food's nutrients in the intestine? (p.12)
10. What is left of the food for us to get rid of? (p.13)

✳ Show how . . .

1. you can make food chains from cards with these words on them – cow, grass, milk, sun, chicken, potato, cereal grain, fish, carrot, human, plankton (p.6)

! Find out more

Look at these other Science in our world books for more information.

Book	Page	Heading
Woodland life	p.8	The green jigsaw
How the Earth works	p.42	Life on land

? Find out from **Book 9: Food**

The number shown like this (p.00) tells you which page to find the answer.

1. What does cooking do to food? (p.14)
2. Why can just warming food, rather than heating it properly be dangerous? (p.14)
3. What is in the milky liquid of boiled rice? (p.19)
4. How does peeling apples and potatoes affect their use as a food? (p.23)
5. What happens to food that is boiled? (p.23)
6. Are snacks good for you? (p.33)
7. Why do food makers use fat instead of water? (p.34)
8. How can food be kept free from microbes? (p.38 and 39)
9. How is cheese made? (p.40)
10. How is bread made? (p.41)

✳ Show how . . .

1. you can tell the different herbs and spices used to improve the flavour of food (p.28 and p.29)
2. many common packaged foods contain preservatives and flavour boosters. Look on several labels and make a chart of your findings

! Find out more

Look at these other Science in our world books for more information.

Book	Page	Heading
How things work	p.12	Openers
Electricity and Magnetism	p.16	Heat, light or safety

SCIENCE IN OUR WORLD WORK CARDS
Book 10: Senses

WORK CARD 1		
Smell, touch, taste		
Page	*AT/PoS*	*SoA/Key words*
8-9	2	3a (part)
10-15,		
18-19	2i	behaviour

Equipment
p.11 Selection of foods, table, blindfold
p.13 Safe unbreakable objects
p.15 Salt, sugar, water, vinegar, strong cold tea
p.17 Onion or garlic flavoured food

Assessment Activities
1. How dilute must a liquid be before it cannot be tasted? Using a measuring cylinder and beakers, work out a way of producing a range of dilute solutions for testing. (p.15)
2. How sensitive is the skin on the back of the hand? Drop smaller and smaller pieces of paper on it. Use this method to test other areas of the skin such as the forehead, back of neck, and leg.

WORK CARD 2		
Hearing and seeing		
Page	*AT/PoS*	*SoA/Key words*
22-23	4iv	ear
24-29	2i	behaviour
30-31	KS3, 4i	vision
33	KS3, 4i	vision
34-35	2i	behaviour

Equipment
p.24 Radio
p.25 Woodlice, dish with a cover to put over half of it.
p.31 Torch, dark room mirror

Assessment Activities
1. Can you tell where a sound is coming from? Sit in the middle of a circle of pupils. Put on a blindfold and point to the pupils who click their fingers. Are some people better at this than others?
2. Do woodlice prefer light or dark? Set up a dish with a dark half and a light half. Put six woodlice in the centre of the dish and leave for a number of minutes.

WORK CARD 3		
Control and memory		
Page	*AT/PoS*	*SoA/Key words*
40-41	2i	behaviour
42-43	2	5a (part)
44-45	2i	behaviour

Equipment
p.41 Long pole
p.42 Ruler

Assessment Activities
1. Do people vary in their reaction time? Try the test on p.42 on a number of people. Record the length of ruler passed through the hand as a measure of reaction time.
2. How good are people at remembering 10-20 objects? Set the objects on a tray. Cover them up then let them be seen for only a minute. The pupils then write down how many they can remember.

WORK CARD 1

SCIENCE IN OUR WORLD WORK CARDS
Smell, touch, taste

? Find out from Book 10: Senses

The number shown like this (p.00) tells you which page to find the answer.

1. How do sheep, sharks and dogs use their sense of smell? (p.8 and p.9)
2. How do we use our sense of smell? (p.10)
3. Why do you sniff when you are smelling something? (p.11)
4. Why do you need a sense of touch? (p.12)
5. Which areas of your skin are particularly sensitive to touch? (p.12)
6. What do snails and insects have to help them with their sense of touch? (p.13)
7. What are your taste buds? Draw a tongue and mark on it the positions of the different kinds. (p.14 and p.15)
8. Where do butterflies and catfish have their taste buds? (p.16 and p.17)
9. Where does the pain come from when someone pulls your hair? (p.18)
10. Why do cats and mice have whiskers? (p.19)

✳ Show how . . .

1. good someone's sense of smell is by trying the smell test on p.11
2. good people are at knowing what an object is just by touching it (p.13)

Find out more

Look at these other Science in our world *books for more information.*

Book	Page	Heading
Food	p.10	Mouth-wateringly good
Growing and Changing	p.8	The early years

? Find out from **Book 10: Senses**

The number shown like this (p.00) tells you which page to find the answer.

1. What are sound waves? (p.22)
2. Where do the sound waves go when they enter the ear? (p.23)
3. What range of sounds can we hear? (p.24)
4. What are infrasounds and ultrasounds and which animals use them? (p.24 and p.25)
5. How do animals use echoes? (p.26 and p.27)

6. How does your eye control the amount of light entering it? (p.30 and p.31)
7. Draw a picture of the eye and show where an image will form. (p.31)
8. What are rods and cones and how do they help us see? (p.33)
9. Why do some animals have both eyes facing forwards while others have their eyes on the sides of their heads? (p.34 and p.35)

✳ Show how . . .

1. you can arrange a collection of objects according to the sound they make from low pitched sounds to high pitched sounds (p.24)
2. someone's pupils change size according to how dark or light it is (p.31)

! Find out more

Look at these other Science in our world *books for more information.*

Book	Page	Heading
Sounds and Music	p.20	Finding your way with sound
Light	p.32	The world turned upside down

© 1993 ATLANTIC EUROPE PUBLISHING CO LTD

? Find out from **Book 10: Senses**

The number shown like this (p.00) tells you which page to find the answer.

1. Why is balance vital? (p.40)
2. Which part of your ear helps to keep your balance? (p.40)
3. How do you sense gravity? (p.40)
4. What happens when you feel dizzy? (p.41)
5. How many messages per second reach your brain and spinal cord? (p.42)

6. How are these messages dealt with and why are they dealt with in this way? (p.42)
7. What is a reflex action? (p.43)
8. Name some reflex actions in your body. (p.43)
9. How does a gopher's memory help it to survive? (p.44)
10. Why do moths fly around lamps? (p.44)

✳ Show how . . .

1. your body keeps its balance when you close your eyes while standing up (p.41)
2. the knee jerk reflex works (p.43)

! Find out more

Look at these other Science in our world *books for more information.*

Book	Page	Heading
Falling	p.8	The G force
Computers and Robots	p.6	What is a computer?

© 1993 ATLANTIC EUROPE PUBLISHING CO LTD

WORK CARD 1			WORK CARD 2			WORK CARD 3		
Curves			Supports			Columns and tubes		
Page	*AT/PoS*	*SoA/Key words*	*Page*	*AT/PoS*	*SoA/Key words*	*Page*	*AT/PoS*	*SoA/Key words*
10,12-13, 14,26-30,33	4iii	simple structures	6,8,18	4iii	simple structures	16-17	4iii	simple structures
			22-23	4iii	bridge building	20-21,		
			24-25	4iii	simple structures	36-37,42	4	4c
			34-35	4	4c			
			44-45	2i	support			

Equipment (Work Card 1)
p.10 Large piece of cardboard
p.13 Card, knitting needle, string
p.26 Card, scissors, paperclip

Assessment Activities (Work Card 1)
1. Does the curve of an arch affect its strength? Make arches of different curvature from cardboard and test their strength. (p.15)
2. Is corrugated cardboard stronger than ordinary cardboard? Devise fair tests to find out.

Equipment (Work Card 2)
p.6 Wedge
p.9 Model building blocks
p.19 Two ruler length pieces of wood, one of them with a small square cross section
p.25 Elastic bands, cardboard, scissors, pencil
p.35 Playing cards, table cloth

Assessment Activities (Work Card 2)
1. How does the strength of beams and girders compare? Test the strength of beams and girders made out of materials such as paper, cardboard and plastic.
2. How does the thickness of a cardboard beam affect its strength?

Equipment (Work Card 3)
p.16 Cardboard to roll into columns, building blocks, sheet of paper, piece of wood board to stand on
p.20 Straws, pipe cleaners, scissors
p.21 Sheets of newspaper, sticky tape
p.37 Straws, pipe cleaners, scissors
p.43 Straws, pipe cleaners, paper, sticky tape, scissors

Assessment Activities (Work Card 3)
1. How many columns are needed to support a piece of paper 50 cm square without the paper sagging? (p.16)
2. Can you make a skyscraper to reach the ceiling? Use straws, paper, cardboard, sticky tape, pipe cleaners. Fit a pulley to the top so that a small load in a paper cup can be lifted up from the ground.

WORK CARD **1**

SCIENCE IN OUR WORLD WORK CARDS

Curves

? Find out from Book 11: Shapes and Structures

The number shown like this (p.00) tells you which page to find the answer.

1. Why are curves helpful to engineers? (p.10)
2. What is a crinkle? What is its other name? (p.12)
3. How do crinkles help can-makers, cacti and shellfish? (p.12 and p.13)
4. What is an arch and what is it used for? (p.14)
5. What can cones be used for? (p.26)
6. Why are claws and some teeth cone-shaped? (p.27)
7. How are dishes and domes strong? (p.28)
8. Where are domes used? (p.28 and p.29)
9. Why is a sphere strong? (p.30)
10. Why is a light bulb shaped like a sphere? (p.33)

✳ Show how ...

1. a curved shape is stronger than a flat shape (p.10)
2. you can make corrugated paper (p.13)
3. a cone concentrates a force (p.26)

! Find out more

Look at these other Science in our world *books for more information.*

Book	Page	Heading
Patterns and Shapes	p.34	Symmetry
Measuring	p.16	Circles and spheres

WORK CARD 2 — Supports

? Find out from Book 11: Shapes and Structures

The number shown like this (p.00) tells you which page to find the answer.

1. What is a tapering shape? (p.6)
2. What is special about a triangular shape? (p.6)
3. What is a block and how is its shape useful? (p.8)
4. What are bars and beams and what do they do? (p.18)
5. Where are beams used? (p.18)
6. What is a suspension bridge? (p.22)
7. What makes a cable strong? (p.23)
8. What gives a bicycle wheel and a spider's web their strength? (p.24 and p.25)
9. What is used to support an umbrella and stop a wall collapsing? (p.34 and p.35)
10. Why are leg bones thicker than arm bones? (p.44 and p.45)

✳ Show how . . .

1. patterns of blocks in a wall give strength (p.9)
2. a girder shape gives stronger support than a bar (p.19)
3. elastic band spokes can make a model bicycle wheel (p.25)

! Find out more

Look at these other Science in our world books for more information.

Book	Page	Heading
Patterns and Shapes	p.30	Solid shapes

© 1993 ATLANTIC EUROPE PUBLISHING CO LTD

WORK CARD 3 — Columns and tubes

? Find out from Book 11: Shapes and Structures

The number shown like this (p.00) tells you which page to find the answer.

1. What are columns? Where are they found in nature? (p.16 and p.17)
2. How are trees stronger than stone columns? (p.17)
3. How is a tube different from a column? (p.20)
4. Why are tunnels made as tubes rather than as arches? (p.21)
5. What are the tallest tubes and give an example of one. (p.21)
6. Why is it sometimes better to use a frame than solid material? (p.36)
7. How are frames made to be strong? (p.36)
8. What is the frame put around a building while it is being built or repaired? (p.37)
9. Why does a skyscraper need to be very strong? (p.42)
10. What hangs from the frame in a skyscraper? (p.42)

✳ Show how . . .

1. you can support your body on columns of rolled up cardboard (p.16)
2. you can make a paper chimney reach the ceiling (p.20)

! Find out more

Look at these other Science in our world books for more information.

Book	Page	Heading
Patterns and Shapes	p.32	Making regular solids
Woodland life	p.36	Woodland timekeepers

© 1993 ATLANTIC EUROPE PUBLISHING CO LTD

WORK CARD 1			WORK CARD 2			WORK CARD 3		
Simple machines			Hot and cold materials			Moving liquids and air		
Page	*AT/PoS*	*SoA/Key words*	*Page*	*AT/PoS*	*SoA/Key words*	*Page*	*AT/PoS*	*SoA/Key words*
6-7	4iii	forces act in opposition	34-35	4ii	substances heated	14-15	3 3i 3a,4a	characteristics of materials
8-9	4iii	different types of forces	40	4ii	substances cooled	20, 23,		
10-13,16-17,			41 4	2b		26-27	3i	characteristics of materials
30-33	4iii	forces in opposition	42-43	3iii	heat on materials	44-45	4	4b,5b
			44-45	4	5b			

Equipment

p.10 Strip of wood, thin board, nail, four small pieces of dowel, one large piece of dowel

Assessment Activities

1. How does the strength of Velcro depend upon the area joined together? Use different sizes of Velcro patches to support weights and work out a relationship.
2. How does the length of a lever affect the weight it can lift? Set up a lever on a pivot close to the end of a table. Put a weight on one end and hang weights on the other.

Equipment

Assessment Activities

1. Which mug keeps a drink hottest for longest? Use a selection of mugs, a measuring jug, warm water and a thermometer to find out.
2. How does the heat in the classroom air vary from place to place? Use a thermometer to find out and explain what you find.

Equipment

p.15 Straw, scissors, glass of water
p.22 Two bowls, water, plastic tube
p.26 Two straws with a bendy section, piece of muslin and an elastic band, jar with tight fitting lid. The lid should have two holes in it through which the straws can tightly fit.

Assessment Activity

1. How does the height between the two bowls affect the speed at which the siphon works? Use a measuring cylinder, stop-clock and ruler to find out.

WORK CARD 1

SCIENCE IN OUR WORLD WORK CARDS
Simple machines

? Find out from Book 12: How things work

The number shown like this (p.00) tells you which page to find the answer.

1. What are three ways of keeping a door closed? (p.6 and p.7)
2. How do an axe, a knife and a pair of scissors cut? (p.8 and p.9)
3. What are the two types of locks? How are they different? (p.10 and p.11)
4. How does a bottle opener work? (p.12)
5. How are cans opened? (p.12 and p.13)
6. How does Velcro work? (p.16)
7. What happens when you zip up? (p.17)
8. How can you lift and move a parcel with a trolley? (p.30)
9. How does a crow bar work? (p.31)
10. What is a screw and how does it work on a tap? (p.32 and p.33)

✳ Show how . . .

1. a key opens a padlock. Explain what happens when the padlock is unlocked then locked again (p.10)
2. a pencil sharpener can lift an apple and explain what you see (p.30)

❗ Find out more

Look at these other Science in our world *books for more information.*

Book	Page	Heading
Falling	p.14	Balancing weights
Electricity and Magnetism	p.28	What is magnetism?

SCIENCE IN OUR WORLD WORK CARDS
Hot and cold materials

? Find out from Book 12: How things work

The number shown like this (p.00) tells you which page to find the answer.

1. How hot does a light bulb get? (p.34)
2. What stops the filament from melting and burning up? (p.34)
3. Why is a filament tube cool? (p.25)
4. What happens when a gas is squeezed then allowed to expand? (p.40)
5. Where in a refrigerator is the gas squeezed? Where is it allowed to expand? (p.40)
6. How does a thermal mug work? (p.42)
7. What is a vacuum? How can it help to keep a drink hot? (p.43)
8. What is the purpose of the silvering in a vacuum flask? (p.43)
9. What is the special heating wire in a heater called? (p.44)
10. How is this wire arranged inside a hair drier? (p.45)

✳ Show how . . .

1. you an compare the temperatures of different liquids with a thermometer (p.31)
2. you an cool down a bottle of water by wrapping it in a damp towel. Explain what you find (p.41)

! Find out more

Look at these other Science in our world books for more information.

Book	Page	Heading
Weather	p.40	Mountain weather
Water	p.6	What is water?

© 1993 ATLANTIC EUROPE PUBLISHING CO LTD

SCIENCE IN OUR WORLD WORK CARDS
Moving liquids and air

? Find out from Book 12: How things work

The number shown like this (p.00) tells you which page to find the answer.

1. How does ink leave a felt tip pen, a fountain pen and a ball point pen? (p.14 and p.15)
2. What is an aerosol and how is it made? (p.20)
3. How does a spray bottle work? (p.20)
4. Why is it better to use an air spray bottle than an aerosol can? (p.21)
5. What is a siphon and what is it used for? (p.22)
6. What happens inside a toilet cistern after you have pushed down the lever? (p.23)
7. How does a vacuum cleaner work? (p.26)
8. How does the dust bag in a vacuum cleaner work? (p.27)
9. How does the air move round a convection heater? (p.44)
10. How is air moved through a hair drier? (p.45)

✳ Show how . . .

1. you can make an airbrush and explain how it works (p.21)
2. you can make and use a pooter an explain how it works (p.26)

! Find out more

Look at these other Science in our world books for more information.

Book	Page	Heading
Flight	p.8	Hot air balloons
Falling	p.26	Falling water

© 1993 ATLANTIC EUROPE PUBLISHING CO LTD

WORK CARD 1			WORK CARD 2			WORK CARD 3		
Finding out about fibres			**Putting fibres together**			**Fabrics**		
Page	*AT/PoS*	*SoA/Key words*	*Page*	*AT/PoS*	*SoA/Key words*	*Page*	*AT/PoS*	*SoA/Key words*
6-7,10-12,			22-23	3	3a	32-41,44	3	3a
14-15,16-17	3 3iii	3b origins of	24	3	3b			
		materials	26-27	3	3b			
18-19	3	4b	28	4	4c			
18-19	3	4b						

WORK CARD 1

Equipment

p.7 Magnifying glass, ice cube
p.13 Silk pin cushion

Assessment Activities

1. Does cotton wool hold in heat better than fleece wool? Work out a fair test to find out.
2. Does wet wool keep things warmer than dry wool? At the end of the activity the pupils can read p.33 and compare their results with "Wool makes good gloves - even when wet".

WORK CARD 2

Equipment

p.24 Three pieces of string, hook
p.25 Pieces of coarse string 30 cm long
p.28 and p.29 String

Assessment Activities

1. How strong are yarns made from different fibres? Use weights to find out.
2. Are wet fibres stronger or weaker than dry fibres?

WORK CARD 3

Equipment

p.34 Dry cloths, water, washing up liquid, bowl
p.38 Raspberries, mortar and pestle, white cloth, water
p.42 String, cloth, dye, bucket

Assessment Activity

1. Which fabrics are hard wearing? Pin down squares of different fabrics and rub them with sand paper or drag a nail across them to find out.

WORK CARD 1

SCIENCE IN OUR WORLD WORK CARDS

Finding out about fibres

❓ Find out from **Book 13: Fibres**

The number shown like this (p.00) tells you which page to find the answer.

1. How do the hairs on your head help you? (p.6 and p.7)
2. How many wool fibres are there on a sheep and how fast do they grow? (p.10)
3. Why does silk shine? (p.12)
4. What creatures make silk and what do they use it for? (p.12)
5. Which plants provide useful fibres from their stems and leaves? (p.14 and p.15)
6. Where are the fibres on a coconut and what are they used for? (p.16)
7. Which part of a plant does cotton come from? How is it cleaned? (p.17)
8. From what are nylon and rayon made? (p.19)
9. How are glass fibres made and what are they used for? (p.19)

✳ Show how . . .

1. the hairs on your arm try to keep you warm (p.7)
2. cotton wool can keep things warm by using cups of warm water and a thermometer

❗ Find out more

Look at these other Science in our world books for more information.

Book	Page	Heading
Sounds and Music	p.38	Singing strings
Patterns and Shapes	p.18	Branching

WORK CARD 2 — Putting fibres together

? Find out from Book 13: Fibres

The number shown like this (p.00) tells you which page to find the answer.

1. How are fibres twisted together? (p.22)
2. What fibres can you find in string and rope? (p.22 and p.23)
3. When are fibres at their strongest? (p.24)
4. How are big ropes made? (p.24)
5. What happens to yarn in knitting? (p.26)
6. How is yarn woven? (p.27)
7. What are a loom, a heddle and a shuttle? (p.27)
8. What do knots do? (p.28)
9. Where are the knots on a carpet and what do they do? (p.28)
10. What is the mesh of a net? Why do people who fish for a living use coarse mesh? (p.29)

✳ Show how . . .

1. you can plait string together to make a rope (p.24)
2. you can make a piece of net (p.29)

! Find out more

Look at these other Science in our world books for more information.

Book	Page	Heading
Shapes and Structures	p.38	Nests
Materials	p.42	Composites and laminates

WORK CARD 3 — Fabrics

? Find out from Book 13: Fibres

The number shown like this (p.00) tells you which page to find the answer.

1. How is wool treated to make a hat? What is a fabric? (p.32)
2. What are the best waterproof materials? (p.34)
3. What is the umbrella's trick? (p.35)
4. What is an astronaut's suit made from? Why is it made from this material? (p.36)
5. What clothes are used by a fire fighter? (p.37)
6. Why are coloured substances added to fibres? (p.38)
7. What are natural dyes? Where do man-made dyes come from? (p.39)
8. What are dyes used for? (p.39)
9. How are different patterns put into fabrics? (p.40 and p.41)
10. What fibres would you use for clothes in cold and in warm places? (p.44)

✳ Show how . . .

1. water cannot get through a dry cloth but water with a drop of washing up liquid can get through. Explain what you see (p.34)
2. you can make a dye from raspberries. Use the dye on a white cloth (p.38)

! Find out more

Look at these other Science in our world books for more information.

Book	Page	Heading
Don't throw it away	p.18	Want not, waste a lot
Falling	p.28	Falling gently

REFERENCE CARD

WORK CARD 1			WORK CARD 2			WORK CARD 3		
Plant life			**Animal life**			**Change**		
Page	*AT/PoS*	*SoA/Key words*	*Page*	*AT/PoS*	*SoA/Key words*	*Page*	*AT/PoS*	*SoA/Key words*
7	2	3b	17	2	3a	32-33	2 2iv	5d decay
8	2 2iv	4d sun for food	18-19	2	3, 4c	34-35	2iv	decay
10-12	2iii	habitat	21	2iii	daily change	36-37	2i	plant growth
13-14	2	5a (part)	22-26,			38-39,40,		
16	2	4a (part)	29-31	2	3a	42,44-45	2iii	seasonal change
38-39	2 2iii	4c environmental conditions						

Equipment
p.13 Tray, trees with low branches
p.15 Food dye, beaker of water, celery
p.16 Selection of cut flowers

Assessment Activities
1. Do different kinds of trees have the same animal life in the same numbers? Work out a fair test for shaking low branches (no tree climbing) and record results in a table.
2. Does the speed of water moving through celery depend on the air conditions? Set up an experiment in still air, in draughty air and one in a polythene bag for humid air.

Equipment
p.19 Plastic box with air holes
p.20 Clear piece of plastic
p.21 Magnifying glass
p.24 Plastic jar, piece of wood and stones
p.28 Plaster of Paris, card, paper clip, old spoon, plastic jug, water

Assessment Activities
1. How much food do caterpillars eat in a day? Use a delicate balance to weigh the leaves before and after being exposed to the caterpillars for a day.
2. Are ground hunters active both day and night? Set up pitfall traps in the morning and empty them in the evening, then set up again and empty them in the following morning.

Equipment
p.33 Large jar, sand, sieved garden soil, card, paper clips, earthworms, leaves
p.34 Fruit, polythene bag
p.37 Piece of tree trunk or thick branch
p.42 Autumn leaves
p.43 Twigs, magnifying glass

Assessment Activity
1. What kinds of foods do earthworms prefer? Set up several wormariums and supply each one with a few different foods. Check regularly and discover how much of each is eaten or taken down into the burrows.

 WORK CARD 1

SCIENCE IN OUR WORLD WORK CARDS
Plant life

? Find out from Book 14: Woodland life

The number shown like this (p.00) tells you which page to find the answer.

1. Why should you not pick flowers in a woodland? (p.7)
2. What do plants use sunlight for? (p.8)
3. What tree grows from an acorn? (p.10)
4. What does a seedling do in its first and in its second year? (p.11)
5. What are conditions like for plants in the top and middle layers of wood? (p.12 and p.13)

6. What are stomata and what do they do? (p.14)
7. What is pollen, where is it made and what does it do? (p.16)
8. How do plants store the power that they need for growing? (p.38)
9. What happens to a bluebell when it has nearly finished flowering? (p.39)

✳ Show how . . .

1. you would find out how water goes up a celery stalk. You will have to set up an experiment before you make your presentation. (p.15)
2. you can tell the parts of a flower in several different plants (p.16)

❗ Find out more

Look at these other Science in our world *books for more information.*

Book	Page	Heading
Falling	p.30	Falling naturally
Energy	p.12	Energy for life

? Find out from **Book 14: Woodland life**

The number shown like this (p.00) tells you which page to find the answer.

1. Which insects visit flowers for food? How do they help the plant? (p.17)
2. What is the main eating stage for any insect? (p.18 and p.19)
3. How do snails and slugs spend their days and nights? (p.21)
4. What small animals can you find in the woodland air? (p.22 and p.23)
5. What animals hunt on the woodland floor? (p.24 and p.25)
6. Name two woodland birds and say what they eat. (p.26)
7. Name two mammals that live in woodland areas. (p.29)
8. What does an owl have on its feet? Why are their feet like this? (p.30)
9. Why can't a mouse hear an owl as it approaches? (p.30)
10. What is an owl pellet? (p.31)

✳ Show how . . .

1. you can set up a pitfall trap and explain what you might expect to catch (p.24)
2. you can make a cast of an animal track (p.28)

! Find out more

Look at these other Science in our world *books for more information.*

Book	Page	Heading
Flight	p.22	Wings of many parts
Senses	p.34	Eyes and lifestyle

© 1993 ATLANTIC EUROPE PUBLISHING CO LTD

WORK CARD **3**

SCIENCE IN OUR WORLD WORK CARDS
Change

? Find out from **Book 14: Woodland Life**

The number shown like this (p.00) tells you which page to find the answer.

1. What happens to dead or discarded materials on the woodland floor? (p.32)
2. Name three kinds of living things which feed on dead material. (p.32 and p.33)
3. Where do fungi get their food from? (p.34)
4. What are lichens and where can they be found? (p.35)
5. What information can a cut tree trunk tell you? (p.36 and p.37)
6. Which plants are the first to flower on the woodland floor in spring? Why do they flower so early? (p.38 and p.39)
7. How do plants change in early summer? (p.40)
8. How do deciduous trees change in autumn? (p.42)
9. Why can laurel and holly keep their leaves in winter? (p.44)
10. How do a dormouse and a butterfly spend the winter? (p.45)

✳ Show how . . .

1. you can set up a wormarium. Explain how to look after it and predict what you might expect to happen to it (p.33)
2. you can tell the age of a piece of tree trunk or thick branch (p.37)

! Find out more

Look at these other Science in our world *books for more information.*

Book	Page	Heading
Don't throw it away	p.42	Heaps of good news
Growing and Changing	p.44	Flowering and fruiting

© 1993 ATLANTIC EUROPE PUBLISHING CO LTD

WORK CARD 1			WORK CARD 2			WORK CARD 3		
How we grow			Starting life			Changes in animals and plants		
Page	*AT/PoS*	*SoA/Key words*	*Page*	*AT/PoS*	*SoA/Key words*	*Page*	*AT/PoS*	*SoA/Key words*
8-9,10-12, 16,22-23,25	2 2ii	3a growth	6-7,26,28, 40,42	2i	growth and reproduction	18-20, 27,29,31-35 39 40	2i 2i 2	growth behaviour 3c

WORK CARD 1

Equipment

p.10 Tracing paper
p.11 Large sheets of paper, felt tip pens of different colours
p.12 Two metre rules, a right-angled piece of wood
p.15 Bathroom scales, scissors
p.17 Mirror
p.25 Family photograph album

Assessment Activities

1. How does your weight vary through the day? (p.15)
2. What is the average height of people in each year in your school?
3. On average, who are the tallest in each year – boys or girls? Make a prediction by just looking at each class before you start measuring.

WORK CARD 2

Equipment

p.9 Aquarium tank with water and plants
p.41 Jar, cotton wool, beans

Assessment Activities

1. What happens to caterpillars when they hatch out? Look for butterfly and moth eggs on the undersides of leaves. Count and draw them and observe them every few days. Follow the lives of the caterpillars which hatch out from them.
2. How does temperature affect the way seeds germinate and grow into seedlings?

WORK CARD 3

Equipment

p.21 Sand, tray, plaster of Paris, water, old spoon and bowl
p.35 Fish scales, magnifying glass or microscope and slide

Assessment Activities

1. How does the amount of light affect the growth of seedlings? Work out a test using varying degrees of illumination. Try to select sites where the temperature is similar.
2. How quickly do stick insects grow? Set up a colony in an old aquarium tank. Feed them on privet and measure the length of the young ones regularly.

WORK CARD 1

SCIENCE IN OUR WORLD WORK CARDS
How we grow

? Find out from Book 15: Growing and Changing

The number shown like this (p.00) tells you which page to find the answer.

1. What is one of the first senses a baby develops. (p.8 and p.9)
2. In what ways do we vary from one another? (p.10)
3. When do people reach their full height? (p.12)
4. Is growth steady or does it happen in fits and starts? (p.12)
5. When do babies get their teeth and how many do they get? (p.16)
6. When do people get their second set of teeth? Why do the wisdom teeth come later? (p.16)
7. What is "filling out"? How does it occur in men and women? (p.22 and p.23)
8. What are hormones and what do they do? (p.23)
9. In what ways do people change in their later years? (p.25)

✳ Show how . . .

1. you can see if the proportions of human bodies change as they get older (p.11)
2. you can look in a mirror and name your teeth. (You should have four incisor teeth in each jaw and next to them on each side a pointed canine tooth then molars behind them) (p.16)

! Find out more

Look at these other Science in our world books for more information.

Book	Page	Heading
Senses	p.10	What can you smell?
Food	p.42	When food is short

❓ Find out from **Book 15: Growing and Changing**

The number shown like this (p.00) tells you which page to find the answer.

1. How did we begin life? (p.6)
2. When do we grow fastest and how does our weight change? (p.6)
3. How long does it take for a baby to grow inside its mother? How does the baby get its food and oxygen? (p.7)
4. How can a baby's airways be cleaned when it is born? (p.7)
5. What are the jobs of the yolk and the white in an egg? (p.26)

6. How does a chick get out of an egg? (p.26)
7. How many eggs does a female frog produce? Where does she leave them? (p.28)
8. What happens to the black centre of a frog's egg? (p.28)
9. How does a seed change when it starts to show signs of life? (p.40)
10. What happens when a bud bursts? (p.42)

✳ Show how . . .

1. a baby rests inside its mother (p.7)
2. you can find out how much water different dry seeds take in when they germinate

❗ Find out more

Look at these other Science in our world books for more information.

Book	Page	Heading
Reproduction and Heredity	p.6	Variety of life
Woodland life	p.38	The first signs of spring

© 1993 Atlantic Europe Publishing Co Ltd

❓ Find out from **Book 15: Growing and Changing**

The number shown like this (p.00) tells you which page to find the answer.

1. How do bones change as we grow? (p.18 and p.19)
2. How do feet change as you grow? (p.20)
3. How does a chick grow in the nest? (p.27)
4. How do tadpoles change as they grow into frogs? (p.29)
5. What changes does a caterpillar go through before it can fly as a butterfly? (p.31)

6. Why does a snake moult and what happens when it does? (p.32)
7. How do razor shells and mussel shells grow? (p.33)
8. What does a new born fish look like? What changes take place as it grows? (p.34 and p.35)
9. How do some animals change to defend their territory? (p.39)
10. How does a chestnut tree change as it sprouts? (p.40)

✳ Show how . . .

1. a tadpole changes as it grows into a frog. Make some drawings to show these changes (p.29)
2. a seed germinates and grows. Plant a number of similar seeds a few days apart to show the different stages (p.41)

❗ Find out more

Look at these other Science in our world books for more information.

Book	Page	Heading
Shapes and Structures	p.44	Our strong shapes
Woodland life	p.18	Fast food feeders

© 1993 Atlantic Europe Publishing Co Ltd

WORK CARD 1			WORK CARD 2			WORK CARD 3		
Time and living things			Measuring time			The Universe		
Page	*AT/PoS*	*SoA/Key words*	*Page*	*AT/PoS*	*SoA/Key words*	*Page*	*AT/PoS*	*SoA/Key words*
6	2i	behaviour	16-17	4iii	forces	8-9	2iii	seasons
12-13	2iii	influenced by	18	4v	path of sun	10-11	4	4e
		environment	20,23,25	4iii	forces	38-39	4v	position of moon
14-15	2i	ideas about	26	4i	circuits	40-41	4v	order of planets
		reproduction	34	3 3ii	atoms			
36-37	2ii	fossils						

Equipment

p.6 Stopwatch

p.12 Cross-section of a piece of tree trunk or thick branch

p.37 Fossils

Assessment Activity

1. How does your pulse change with your activity? Lie down and take your pulse for 30 seconds; multiply your score by two to find the beats per minute. Repeat twice more and find an average. Now find your pulse rate when sitting up, standing up and after walking for a minute.

Equipment

p.17 Two plastic containers - one with a small hole in it, water, stopclock, 4 long pieces of wood, 4 shorter pieces of wood, 2 sheets of cardboard (one for making triangles), glass cylinder, float, piece of dowel, 2 eye hooks, wire, tall glass cylinder, plastic tube to form siphon from large container such as a bucket, small tap for plastic tube

p.18 Stick, stones, open ground in sunny position

p.21 Cardboard, tracing paper, string, weight, strip of wood, straw or small wooden rod for toothed wheel axle, support for escapement and toothed wheel axle

Equipment

None

Assessment Activity

None

Assessment Activity (Card 2)

Can you make a clepsydra from your own design? Use the picture on p.17 for ideas then make one using different materials.

 WORK CARD **1**

SCIENCE IN OUR WORLD WORK CARDS
Time and living things

? Find out from Book 16: Time

The number shown like this (p.00) tells you which page to find the answer.

1. Name one type of body "clock". (p.6)
2. What is a circadian rhythm? (p.6)
3. How often does a tree make a ring? What can tree rings tell us? (p.12)
4. How old are the oldest trees? Where do they live? (p.13)
5. What is a lifespan? What is the average lifespan in developed and in developing countries? (p.14)
6. Which organisms have the shortest lifespans? How many generations of bacteria can be produced in a day? (p.15)
7. What may happen to a species over millions of years? (p.36)
8. What was first used to measure the age of rocks? Give two examples. (p.37)
9. When did the first dinosaurs appear on Earth? How long was the Age of Reptiles? (p.37)

✳ Show how . . .

1. you can work out a real or imaginary family tree (p.14)
2. you can make a ecological record of time using one centimetre for each million years (p.36)

! Find out more

Look at these other Science in our world books for more information.

Book	Page	Heading
Changing and Growing	p.24	Growing older
How the Earth works	p.6	Tracing the Earth's story

WORK CARD 2

? Find out from Book 16: Time

The number shown like this (p.00) tells you which page to find the answer.

1. What old time keepers were used to measure a few hours? (p.16)
2. What old time keepers were used for measuring shorter periods of time? (p.16 and p.17)
3. What is a shadow clock? What is a more accurate form of it? (p.18)
4. What do a.m. and p.m. mean? (p.18)
5. What kinds of clocks replaced sun dials? How could people tell the time by them? (p.19)
6. Why is the pendulum a good time keeper? (p.20)
7. How does a pendulum clock work? (p.23)
8. How does a spring-driven clock work? (p.25)
9. How does a quartz watch work? (p.26)
10. What sort of clocks are used to set the 'pips' on the radio? How accurate are these clocks? (p.34)

✻ Show how . . .

1. you can measure time with a water clock (p.17)
2. you can make a clock with a pendulum (p.22 and p.23)

! Find out more

Look at these other Science in our world books for more information.

Book	Page	Heading
Falling	p.18	Swinging about
Measuring	p.22	Speed and acceleration

© 1993 ATLANTIC EUROPE PUBLISHING CO LTD

WORK CARD 3

? Find out from Book 16: Time

The number shown like this (p.00) tells you which page to find the answer.

1. How do plants and animals change with the seasons? (p.8 and p.9)
2. What is a calendar? What was used to make the first one? (p.10)
3. What was the Babylonian calendar? How did the Egyptians improve it? What sort of calendar do we use today? (p.10 and p.11)
4. Why do we have days and nights, years and months? (p.10 and p.11)
5. How fast does light travel? How can this information be used to measure the distance of the moon from the Earth? (p.38 and p.39)
6. Arrange the planets in order of day length starting with the planet with the shortest day length. Does this match the order of size of the planets starting with the largest? (p.40 and p.41)
7. Arrange the planets in order of year length starting with the planet with the shortest year length. Does this match the order of planet distances from the Sun starting with the planet nearest the Sun? (p.40 and p.41)

✻ Show how . . .

1. plants and animals change with the seasons with a series of pictures. Make a big drawing of the picture on p.10 and p.11 and stick on your plant and animal pictures around the correct pictures of the Earth

! Find out more

Look at these other Science in our world books for more information.

Book	Page	Heading
Energy	p.8	Energy from the Sun
The Earth in Space	p.42	Galaxies

© 1993 ATLANTIC EUROPE PUBLISHING CO LTD

WORK CARD 1			WORK CARD 2			WORK CARD 3		
Energy and the sun			Air, water and food			Fuels		
Page	*AT/PoS*	*SoA/Key words*	*Page*	*AT/PoS*	*SoA/Key words*	*Page*	*AT/PoS*	*SoA/Key words*
6-7	4	4b,5b	14-15,18-19,			24	4	4b
8-12,16-17	4ii	energy transfer	22-23,26-27	4ii	energy transfers	30,32-33	4	3b
						34-35	4	5c
						36-37	4	5b
						39	4ii	range of fuels
						42-43	4	5c

Equipment

p.6 Torch
p.9 Radiometer
p.10 Two plastic bottles, white paint, black paint, paintbrush, two thermometers

Assessment Activity

1. Does the colour of the surface under an ice cube affect the way the ice cube melts in the Sun? Place a number of ice cubes each on a different coloured plastic plate. Time how long each ice cube takes to melt.

Equipment

p.20 Stiff cardboard, length of wire, large diameter cardboard tube, wooden frame or other form of support
p.22 Cotton reel, pieces of card or plastic, wire supports
p.27 Cake dish, sand tray, cotton string, vegetable oils

Assessment Activities

1. Can you make a windmill lift a weight? Make a paper windmill. Attach its centre to a straw axle. Stick a 30 cm long piece of string to the straw and add a piece of Plasticine to the string. Support the windmill and axle and time how long it takes to raise the weight when the windmill is blown with a hair drier.
2. What is the smallest windmill you can make that lifts the weight?

Equipment

p.24 Elastic band, hooks, two pieces of dowel, card, four pieces of wood shaped as the picture shows, table-tennis ball.

Assessment Activity

1. Do different candles produce different amounts of heat energy? Compare a household candle and a beeswax candle by using wax to stick pins on a length of wire and inserting one end in the candle flame. Time how long it takes for each candle to melt the wax so that the pins fall off.

? Find out from **Book 17: Energy**

The number shown like this (p.00) tells you which page to find the answer.

1. What do people really mean when they say that energy has been 'used up'? (p.6)
2. What energy changes take place as a car moves along? (p.6 and p.7)
3. What forms of energy does the Sun radiate to Earth? What does radiate mean? (p.8)
4. What happens when light shines on to bright objects and on to dark objects? (p.10)
5. How does a crocodile warm up and cool down? (p.11)
6. Why are plants green? (p.12)
7. What does chlorophyll do? (p.12)
8. What would we have if we could harness the Sun's energy? (p.16)
9. Describe three ways that solar power can be collected. (p.17)

✳ Show how . . .

1. energy changes when you switch on a torch (p.7)
2. you would set up an experiment to see how a black bottle and a white bottle are affected by solar radiation. Predict what might happen and explain your prediction. (p.11)

! Find out more

Look at these other Science in our world books for more information.

Book	Page	Heading
Light	p.6	Sunlight
Measuring	p.32	Temperature

❓ Find out from **Book 17: Energy**

The number shown like this (p.00) tells you which page to find the answer.

1. What makes sea water circulate? What energy does it carry? (p.14)
2. How does energy change in the water cycle? (p.15)
3. Where does the Earth's atmosphere get its heat from? (p.18)
4. How is wind energy used? (p.19)
5. What energy changes take place at a waterfall? (p.22)
6. What is an HEP plant? (p.23)
7. How can engineers match the electricity they produce to the amount that people need? (p.23)
8. Which foods contain most energy? (p.26)
9. Why do you feel tired after exercise? (p.27)

✳ Show how . . .

1. you can test the wind for energy using a rotor (p.20 and p.21)
2. oil contains energy by doing the investigation on p.26. Explain what you see

❗ Find out more

Look at these other Science in our world *books for more information.*

Book	Page	Heading
Weather	p.7	When the Sun shines
Food	p.36	Weight watching

© 1993 Atlantic Europe Publishing Co Ltd

❓ Find out from **Book 17: Energy**

The number shown like this (p.00) tells you which page to find the answer.

1. What is the problem with most forms of natural energy? (p.24)
2. What is an energy supply called? (p.24)
3. Why can coal produce more heat energy than wood? (p.30)
4. What is petroleum? How did it form? (p.32)
5. What happens to crude oil when it is refined? (p.33)
6. What do people in developing countries use for fuel? How do these fuels affect the environment? (p.34)
7. What are the side effects of burning fossil fuels? (p.35)
8. What energy changes take place inside a power station? (p.39)
10. How can energy be saved in the home? (p.42 and p.43)

✳ Show how . . .

1. you can use the stored energy in an elastic band to move a table-tennis ball. You could make the model on p.26 or make a model of your own design
2. some places around your school are wasting energy (p.43)

❗ Find out more

Look at these other Science in our world *books for more information.*

Book	Page	Heading
Don't throw it away	p.40	Don't throw heat away
How the Earth works	p.12	The Earth's natural cycles

© 1993 Atlantic Europe Publishing Co Ltd

WORK CARD 1			WORK CARD 2			WORK CARD 3		
Distance and speed			Area and volume			Measurements on air and water		
Page	*AT/PoS*	*SoA/Key words*	*Page*	*AT/PoS*	*SoA/Key words*	*Page*	*AT/PoS*	*SoA/Key words*
6-9,22-23	1	practical skill	10-12,			24	3i	properties of a gas
28-29	3i	liquid/gas properties	14,16,17	1	practical skills	26-27	3i	properties of a liquid
						32-33	1	practical skills
						40-41	3	5b
						42	3	4c
						43	2iii	human activity

Equipment

p.9 Bicycle, chalk

Assessment Activities

1. What is the length of the playground or school hall? Make a guess then use a bicycle wheel odometer to find out the true length. (p.9)
2. Measure the length of a local footpath. (Do not use an odometer on the road.).

Equipment

p.11 Squared paper
p.13 Card
p.15 Two measuring jugs, salt

Assessment Activities

1. What is the volume of a certain weight of dried peas? Make a volume measurer as shown on p.13 and one of the balances on p.18 and p.19. Does the same volume of dried beans weigh the same as the peas. How do the volumes of other dried foods compare?
2. How does the area of a leaf change as it grows? Use a squared card to press below a growing leaf on a bush or seedling and draw around the leaf. Repeat this every few days.

Equipment

p.24 Balloon, jar, card, sticky tape, wire, wooden support
p.26 Clear plastic tube, T-piece, card
p.41 Uncooked red cabbage, distilled water, cooker and pan, filter paper and funnel, jars or beakers, range of household liquids (not bleach or strong oven cleaner)
p.43 Beaker, filter paper, area of ground where rain collector can be left out safely

Assessment Activity

? Find out from Book 18: Measuring

The number shown like this (p.00) tells you which page to find the answer.

1. With which units are length, weight and volume measured in the metric and imperial systems? (p.5)
2. What are the major divisions in the metric system on a ruler? What are the minor divisions? (p.6)
3. Name four different types of ruler. (p.6 and p.7)
4. What is used to measure the width of a curved solid object? (p.8)
5. What is an odometer? Where would you find it on a car? (p.9)
6. What is speed and what is acceleration? (p.22)
7. Explain how you would work out the speed of an object. (p.22)
8. How is acceleration measured in motorbikes and automobiles? (p.23)
9. How can you tell if a colourless liquid or gas is flowing? (p.28 and p.29)

✳ Show how . . .

1. you could measure the thickness of someone's arm with two pieces of cardboard, a paper fastener and a file (p.8)
2. you could work out the speed of a toy car running along a table top (p.23)

! Find out more

Look at these other Science in our world *books for more information.*

Book	Page	Heading
Starting and Stopping	p.14	Pushing for a start
Science and Design	p.18	Testing your reach

WORK CARD 2

Area and volume

? Find out from Book 18: Measuring

The number shown like this (p.00) tells you which page to find the answer.

1. What does the word 'area' mean? (p.10)
2. What is the difference between a square and a rectangle? How would you find their areas? (p.10 and p.11)
3. How could you measure the area of an irregular shape? (p.11)
4. What does the word 'volume' mean? (p.12)
5. How can you work out the volume of a cube? (p.12)
6. How could you work out the volume of a turtle? (p.14)
7. Write the Greek letter pi and the amount it is nearly equal to. (p.16)
8. What is the circumference of a wheel with a radius of 30 cm? (p.16)
9. What is the volume of a football of radius 12 cm? (p.16)
10. What is the area of a circular table top of 45 cm radius? (p.16)

✳ Show how . . .

1. you can work out the area of your footprint (p.11)
2. you can find the volume of a small doll (p.11)
3. you can calculate the circumference and volume of the Earth (p.17)

! Find out more

Look at these other Science in our world books for more information.

Book	Page	Heading
Patterns and Shapes	p.30	Solid shapes
Science and Design	p.42	Designing a kitchen

WORK CARD 3

Measurements on air and water

? Find out from Book 18: Measuring

The number shown like this (p.00) tells you which page to find the answer.

1. What do meteorologists call a place where air builds up? (p.24)
2. What do meteorologists call a place where air flows away? (p.24)
3. What is used to measure air pressure? (p.24)
4. What will a manometer measure? (p.26)
5. How is blood pressure measured? (p.27)
6. How do the Fahrenheit and Celsius scales differ? (p.32 and p.33)
7. What is an acid? What is an alkali? (p.40)
8. What is an indicator? How does it work? (p.40)
9. What causes acid rain? What colour does acid rain turn an indicator? (p.42)
10. How could you find out how dirty rainwater is? (p.43)

✳ Show how . . .

1. you can make a simple barometer (p.25)
2. you can make an indicator and test it on a few safe household liquids. You will need an adult to help you prepare the red cabbage before your investigation (p.41)

! Find out more

Look at these other Science in our world books for more information.

Book	Page	Heading
Weather	p.42	Forecasting the weather
Water	p.8	Where water comes from

WORK CARD 1
The Earth's structure

Page	AT/PoS	SoA/Key words
8-9,10-11, 14-15,16	3iv	geological events
19	3iv	natural materials
20-23	3iv	geological events

Equipment

p.10 and p.11 Large piece of paper, ruler
p.22 Sheets of different coloured Plasticine

Assessment Activity

1. Can you make a model volcano? Use a small bottle with a narrow neck. Spoon some sodium bicarbonate into the bottle, add a measured volume of vinegar (eye protection should be worn). Wait for the build-up of gas to give an 'eruption'. Work out the best mixture of ingredients to give the best 'eruption'.

WORK CARD 2
Rocks and soil

Page	AT/PoS	SoA/Key words
24-25	3iv	natural materials
26-27	3	3c, 4e
28-31	3iv	natural materials
38-39	3iv	how soil develops

Equipment

p.25 Selection of rocks
p.29 Sand, small pieces of brass, shallow dish, bucket of water
p.39 Soil, card, forceps, microscope and slides

Assessment Activity

1. Does soil from different places contain the same living things?
Collect soil samples from different places and examine them as described on p.39. What do you find?

WORK CARD 3
Natural cycles

Page	AT/PoS	SoA/Key words
12-13	3iii	origins of materials
14-15	3iv	geological events
26	3	3b, 4e
33	3iv	weather
42-43	2	4d
44-45	2	3b

Equipment

p.43 Pictures of local animals and plants, large sheets of paper for poster

Assessment Activity

1. How does fertiliser affect soil water? Set up a number of jars of soil and water. Put different amounts of fertiliser into the jars and leave one jar without fertiliser. Put them all in a sunny position and record the changes that you notice over a few weeks.

 WORK CARD **1**
SCIENCE IN OUR WORLD WORK CARDS
The Earth's structure

? Find out from **Book 19: How the Earth works**

The number shown like this (p.00) tells you which page to find the answer.

1. How old is the planet Earth? How did it form? (p.8 and p.9)
2. How much space dust lands on Earth each year? (p.9)
3. What is at the centre of the Earth? (p.10)
4. Where is the mantle? How is it different from the Earth's crust? (p.10 and p.11)
5. How does the mantle affect the crust? (p.14 and p.15)

6. What do the moving plates cause? (p.16)
7. What are the two kinds of volcanic eruptions? How do they differ? (p.19)
8. What causes an earthquake? (p.20)
9. What are the two ways that mountains can form? (p.22)
10. Why do mountains remain tall for such long periods of time? (p.23)

✳ Show how . . .

1. the inside of the Earth looks to scale by making a picture. Use 1 cm = 100 km (p.10 and p.11)
2. rocks get folded inside mountains by using Plasticine sheets. Explain what causes the rocks to move. (p.22)

Find out more

Look at these other Science in our world books for more information.

Book	Page	Heading
Time	p.30	Navigating with time
Waves and Vibration	p.40	Earthquake

? Find out from Book 19: How the Earth works

The number shown like this (p.00) tells you which page to find the answer.

1. What are metamorphic rocks? What might you find in them? (p.24)
2. What are igneous rocks? Give three ways in which they form. (p.25)
3. How do sedimentary rocks form? (p.26)
4. What is the rock cycle? What stage of the cycle is shown in the picture? (p.27)
5. How do minerals form? (p.28)

6. What is an ore? Where are the richest ores found? (p.28)
7. What are veins? Which metals can be found together in some of them? (p.29)
8. How was petroleum formed? Why does it collect in special places in the rocks? (p.30 and p.31)
9. What is soil? Why are some soils more fertile than others? (p.38)

✳ Show how . . .

1. you can tell a piece of sedimentary rock from other forms of rock (p.24 and p.25)
2. people pan for gold using a mixture of sand and small pieces of brass, a shallow dish and a bucket of water (p.29)

! Find out more

Look at these other Science in our world books for more information.

Book	Page	Heading
Woodland life	p.32	Nothing goes to waste
Materials	p.8	Raw materials

© 1993 ATLANTIC EUROPE PUBLISHING CO LTD

? Find out from Book 19: How the Earth works

The number shown like this (p.00) tells you which page to find the answer.

1. Arrange the natural cycles in a list starting with the shortest and ending with the longest. Next to each cycle write down how long it takes. (p.12 and p.13)
2. How did the Earth look 250, 100, 50 million years ago? What changes may happen in the future? (p.14 and p.15)
3. Look at p.26 and p.27. What can you see on the mountain that shows the rock cycle in action?

4. Explain how air moves in the atmosphere. (p.33)
5. Why are plants vital? How do they influence the way the Earth works? (p.40)
6. Describe the ways nutrients in plants get into the soil and what happens to them there. (p.42 and p.43)
7. How do people affect the world in which they live? (p.44 and p.45)

✳ Show how . . .

1. you can use pictures to make a food chain in the sea (p.36 and p.37)
2. some ocean currents move round the Earth by using a globe and the map on p.34 and p.35

! Find out more

Look at these other Science in our world books for more information.

Book	Page	Heading
Food	p.6	Why eat food?
Woodland life	p.8	The green jigsaw

© 1993 ATLANTIC EUROPE PUBLISHING CO LTD

WORK CARD 1			WORK CARD 2			WORK CARD 3		
Energy and power			Friction			Moving in air and water		
Page	*AT/PoS*	*SoA/Key words*	*Page*	*AT/PoS*	*SoA/Key words*	*Page*	*AT/PoS*	*SoA/Key words*
6-10	4ii	movement	18,20,			22-27	4iii	forces
12-15	2i	movement	38-39	4iii	forces	28	2i	movement
32-33	4iii	forces	41	4	4c,5d	29	4iii	forces
			42-43,45	4iii	forces	31	2i	movement
						44-45	4iii	forces

Equipment

p.8 Foam board or stiff card, scissors, glue, two cotton reels, dowel, scale pan, string, weights
p.10 Dowel rod, elastic band, string, cardboard tube
p.15 Starting block

Assessment Activity

1. Does a wheelie with solid wheels travel further than one with holes in its wheels? Investigate the idea of reducing the wheelie's mass to make it go further.

Equipment

p.18 and p.19 Wood block, flat surface, pulley, string, weights, scale pan
p.20 Equipment for p.18 and p.19, oil, washing up liquid, soap, petroleum jelly
p.40 Small gyroscope, sharp pencil with a rubber on its end, bicycle with speedometer, playground area, chalk.

Assessment Activity

1. How does friction affect cloth materials? Cut out rectangles of different kinds of cloth. Stick each in turn beneath a block such as the one on p.18 and test with the weights. What do you find?

Equipment

p.30 Thin card, sticky tape, straw, thread, scissors

Assessment Activity

Which Plasticine shape has the greatest drag? Use a long glass tube (spaghetti jar) and dilute wall paper paste (caution – some people are allergic to the chemicals in some pastes), Plasticine, scales and stopwatch to find out.

 **WORK CARD 1**

SCIENCE IN OUR WORLD WORK CARDS
Energy and power

? Find out from **Book 20: Starting and Stopping**

The number shown like this (p.00) tells you which page to find the answer.

1. What are the two sources of energy which can get something moving? Give some examples of each. (p.6)
2. Name two sources of energy for machines. (p.8)
3. What is the source of energy in the 'wheelie'? What happens to this energy source after a while? (p.8 and p.9)
4. Explain how the energy source makes the model dragster move. (p.10)

5. Where is the energy store that an animal uses when it wants to move? How does an animal prepare for a fast start? (p.12)
6. How do the bones and muscles look when the leg is straight? Make a labelled drawing using the picture to help you. (p.13)
7. How does an athlete's body change as she begins a race? (p.14 and p.15)
8. Explain how shoes are designed so that they do not slip. (p.14)

✷ Show how . . .

1. you can make a 'wheelie' and get it to move. Explain where the 'wheelie' gets its energy from (p.8)
2. you can make a model dragster and get it to move. Explain how you put energy into the dragster (p.10 and p.11)

❗ Find out more

Look at these other Science in our world *books for more information.*

Book	Page	Heading
Energy	p.6	Energy in many forms
Don't waste energy	p.44	The world's energy supply

? Find out from Book 20: Starting and Stopping

The number shown like this (p.00) tells you which page to find the answer.

1. Where is there friction on a bicycle? (p.18)
2. What affects friction? What are the two kinds of friction? Which is the stronger of the two? (p.18)
3. What is a lubricant? Give some examples of lubricants. (p.20)
4. How do skiers, cyclists and motorists skid? (p.38)
5. How can skidding be useful? (p.39)

6. What happens when you apply the brakes on a bike? (p.41)
7. Why do tyres need a deep tread for driving in the wet? (p.42)
8. How are highways designed to be safe in wet weather? (p.43)
9. When does a car start to aquaplane? (p.43)
10. What sort of tyres are used on a racing car in dry and in wet weather? (p.45)

✳ Show how . . .

1. moving friction is weaker than starting friction (p.18)
2. a lubricant reduces friction (p.20)

! Find out more

Look at these other Science in our world books for more information.

Book	Page	Heading
How things work	p.32	Turn of the screw
Don't waste energy	p.40	A winning formula

© 1993 Atlantic Europe Publishing Co Ltd

? Find out from Book 20: Starting and Stopping

The number shown like this (p.00) tells you which page to find the answer.

1. What happens when you go forward in air and water? What is the resistance to your movement called? (p.22)
2. When is drag important? How can you check for drag? How can you tell the amount of drag around an object? (p.22 and p.23)
3. What do we call the special shaping to reduce drag? How are aeroplanes and trucks made to reduce drag? (p.24 and p.25)

4. How is a dragster designed to move quickly? (p.26 and p.27)
5. Why is starting and stopping different in water than in air? (p.28)
6. How does a fish make a quick start? (p.28)
7. How do propellers and paddles work? (p.29)
8. In what ways can birds alter their wings? What do these changes do to a bird's movement? (p.31)
9. How does an aircraft slow down? (p.31)

✳ Show how . . .

1. you can test streamlined shapes is by timing how long it takes for several shapes of Plasticine model to fall to the bottom of a tall jar filled with dilute wallpaper paste

! Find out more

Look at these other Science in our world books for more information.

Book	Page	Heading
Flight	p.34	Flying faster than sound
Water	p.30	Secrets of ships

© 1993 Atlantic Europe Publishing Co Ltd

WORK CARD 1			WORK CARD 2			WORK CARD 3		
Patterns to help us			Patterns and living things			Patterns in chemicals		
Page	*AT/PoS*	*SoA/Key words*	*Page*	*AT/PoS*	*SoA/Key words*	*Page*	*AT/PoS*	*SoA/Key words*
6-7	2i	behaviour	10-11	2ii	differences	36-38,40,		
8	4iv	reflection	18	2i	support	42-43	3iii	origins of
9	1	computers	20-21	2ii	similarities			materials
12-13	2i	behaviour	34-35	2ii	differences			
16	4i	circuits	44	2ii	genetic information			

Equipment

p.6 Thin cardboard

p.12 Tracing paper

p.17 Pegboard, five pegs, rubber bands

Assessment Activity

1. Are some letters of the Braille system easier to learn than others? Ask a number of people to learn part or all of the Braille alphabet then test them and record the results.

Equipment

p.11 Ink pad, white paper

p.18 Tracing paper, leaves

p.21 Turntable, cotton reel, cardboard, scissors, pencil

p.34 Mirror

p.35 Eggs

Assessment Activity

1. Can leaves be divided into two groups according to the way the veins branch? Make a collection of leaves and find out. (Monocotyledons have parallel veins and dicotyledons have branching veins.)

Equipment

p.38 salt, dark paper, magnifying glass

Assessment Activity

1. Can you make crystals? Make solutions of salt, sugar and bath crystals. Leave them to evaporate. How does the concentration of the solution affect crystal growth? How does the temperature of the drying area affect crystal growth?

WORK CARD **1**

SCIENCE IN OUR WORLD WORK CARDS

Patterns to help us

? Find out from **Book 21: Patterns and Shapes**

The number shown like this (p.00) tells you which page to find the answer.

1. What did Louis Braille invent? Where did he get his idea from? (p.6)
2. How is the Morse code different from the Braille system? (p.7)
3. What is an abacus and how is it used? (p.8)
4. What is a bar code and where do you find them? (p.8)
5. How can a computer read a number on a bar code? (p.8)

6. What pattern does a computer understand? What special number system does a computer use? (p.9)
7. What is a route? How are they made easier to follow? (p.12 and p.13)
8. Why should someone want to find the shortest distance between two places? (p.12)
9. What is a printed circuit? How is it designed? (p.16)
10. Name three things which have printed circuits.

✳ Show how . . .

1. you can make a message in Braille (p.7)
2. you can make a simple route from your home to your school (p.12)

 Find out more

Look at these other Science in our world books for more information.

Book	Page Heading
Senses	p.12 Keeping in touch
Electricity and Magnetism	p.18 All in a line

? Find out from Book 21: Patterns and Shapes

The number shown like this (p.00) tells you which page to find the answer.

1. What are the three basic types of fingerprints? Draw an example of each type. (p.10 and p.11)
2. What sort of pattern is branching? (p.18)
3. Where can you find examples of branching in nature? (p.18)
4. Who discovered some rules about branching? Complete the list on p.18.
5. Name some living things which have a spiral arrangement. (p.20)
6. What type of spiral is made by the winds in a tropical storm? (p.21)
7. How can you tell if something has one plane of symmetry? (p.34)
8. What is turning symmetry? Why does a sea urchin have it and a marble doesn't? (p.35)
9. Why carries the information for living things to be created? What does it look like? (p.44)

✳ Show how . . .

1. you can take someone's fingerprints and discover what patterns they have (p.10 and p.11)
2. you can arrange objects in two groups – symmetrical and unsymmetrical (p.34 and p.35)

! Find out more

Look at these other Science in our world books for more information.

Book	Page Heading
Growing and Changing	p.20 Familiar feet
Reproduction and Heredity	p.10 Genes

© 1993 ATLANTIC EUROPE PUBLISHING CO LTD

? Find out from Book 21: Patterns and Shapes

The number shown like this (p.00) tells you which page to find the answer.

1. What is everything in the Universe made from? (p.36)
2. What is an element? Give an example of one. How many elements are there? (p.36)
3. What is a compound? (p.36)
4. What is a molecule? (p.37)
5. Why do snowflakes have six sided patterns? (p.37)
6. What is a crystal? (p.38)
7. Why does salt have a cubic crystal? (p.38)
8. What are many rocks made from? What instrument is needed to find this out? (p.40)
9. How can chemists make new chemicals? (p.42)
10. How is the gas called ethylene turned into a solid called polythene? (p.42 and p.43)

✳ Show how . . .

1. you can make a molecule model with straws and different coloured Plasticine
2. you can grow crystals quickly. Make a very strong solution of Epsom salt. Put a drop on a microscope slide and warm it near a lamp. Look at the white rim of the drying drop with a magnifying glass or microscope

! Find out more

Look at these other Science in our world books for more information.

Book	Page Heading
Water	p.6 What is water?
How the Earth works	p.24 Rocks in mountains.

© 1993 ATLANTIC EUROPE PUBLISHING CO LTD

WORK CARD 1			WORK CARD 2			WORK CARD 3		
The planets of the solar system			The Moon			From Earth to space		
Page	*AT/PoS*	*SoA/Key words*	*Page*	*AT/PoS*	*SoA/Key words*	*Page*	*AT/PoS*	*SoA/Key words*
8-9, 34-37	4v	order of planets	16-17	4	2e	10	3i	gases
			18-19	4	4e (part)	12-13,		
Equipment			20-21	4v	eclipse	32-33	4v	sun
none			23	4iii	gravity	38-44	4v	night sky
			29-31	3iii	origin of material			
Assessment Activity			37	4	night sky	**Equipment**		
None						None		

Equipment

p.17 Battery, wires, bulb, plywood, stiff wire, golf ball, model Earth, wood for spindles, strong sticky tape
p.23 Bowl of water, permanganate of potash crystals

Assessment Activity

1. How quickly do the phases of the moon change? Draw the moon every night for a month and date each picture. If it is cloudy, draw how you predict the moon to be. On the next clear night compare how the moon appears with your predictions.

Assessment Activity

1. Can you make craters in plaster of Paris? Wear eye protection. Mix up the powder and the water. Pour it into a dish and drop in aquarium gravel 'meteoroids' at regular intervals of time. How long does it take for a meteoroid to leave a crater and be completely covered by the plaster?

WORK CARD 1

SCIENCE IN OUR WORLD WORK CARDS
The planets of the solar system

? Find out from Book 22: The Earth in space

The number shown like this (p.00) tells you which page to find the answer.

1. How did the planet Earth form? (p.8)
2. Where are the magnetic North and South poles? (p.9)
3. What are conditions like on Venus? (p.34)
4. What is the temperature on Mercury? What substances are found in Mercury's atmosphere? (p.35)
5. What are conditions like on Mars? (p.35)
6. How does Pluto differ from Mercury? (p.35)
7. What substances make up Jupiter? How are they arranged? (p.36)
8. How is Saturn similar to Jupiter and how is it different? (p.37)
9. What substances are found on Uranus and how are they arranged? (p.37)
10. How is Neptune similar to Uranus and how is it different? (p.37)

✳ Show how . . .

1. the sizes of the planets compare by making scale models from cardboard discs
2. the planets vary by colouring in discs and explaining what can be seen on each planet surface

! Find out more

Look at these other Science in our world *books for more information.*

Book	Page	Heading
How the Earth works	p.16	The crustal plates today
Time	p.40	Planet time

? Find out from **Book 22: The Earth in space**

The number shown like this (p.00) tells you which page to find the answer.

1. Where does moonlight come from? (p.18)
2. What are the phases of the Moon from new Moon to full Moon? (p.18 and p.19)
3. How are the Earth, Moon and Sun arranged when the moon is new and when it is full? (p.18 and p.19)
4. What causes an eclipse of the Sun? (p.20)
5. What causes an eclipse of the Moon? (p.20)
6. Which part of the Sun can be seen during a solar eclipse? (p.21)
7. How does the Moon affect water in the oceans? (p.23)
8. How did the Moon's craters form? What made the surface of the land smooth? (p.31)
9. Where else in the Solar System can you find moons? (p.37)

✳ Show how . . .

1. the Earth and Moon move around the Sun by making the orrery on p.16 and p.17
2. the phases of the moon change by making a flick book using the outer ring of illustrations on p.18 and p.19 to help you

❗ Find out more

Look at these other Science in our world *books for more information.*

Book	Page	Heading
Time	p.38	Distance and time
Light	p.14	Reflections everywhere

© 1993 ATLANTIC EUROPE PUBLISHING CO LTD

? Find out from **Book 22: The Earth in space**

The number shown like this (p.00) tells you which page to find the answer.

1. Arrange the natural cycles in a list starting with the shortest and ending with the longest . Next to each cycle write down how long it takes. (p.1 to p.13)
2. How did the Earth look 250, 100 and 50 million years ago? What changes may happen in the future? (p.14 and 15)
3. Look at pages 26 and 27. What can you see on the mountain that shows the rock cycle in action? (p.26 and p.27)
4. What are the four ecosystems shown on the map on page 34? What is a feature of the climate in each of them? (p.34)
5. Why are plants vital? How do they influence the way the Earth works? (p.40)
6. Describe the ways nutrients in plants get into the soil and what happens to them there. (p.42 and p.43)
7. How do people affect the world in which they live? (p.44 and p.45)

✳ Show how . . .

1. a comet's orbit around the Sun is different from a planet's orbit (p.40 and p.41)
2. a star forms and eventually becomes a black dwarf by making a flick book (p.44 and p.45)

❗ Find out more

Look at these other Science in our world *books for more information.*

Book	Page	Heading
Energy	p.8	Energy from the Sun
How the Earth works	p.32	The atmosphere

© 1993 ATLANTIC EUROPE PUBLISHING CO LTD

WORK CARD 1			WORK CARD 2			WORK CARD 3		
How we vary			Forces and design			Problems of design		
Page	*AT/PoS*	*SoA/Key words*	*Page*	*AT/PoS*	*SoA/Key words*	*Page*	*AT/PoS*	*SoA/Key words*
6-15,38	2ii	differences	20-29	4iii	forces	30-35	4iii	forces
16,18	2i	good health				36-37	3	3a
						40-43	3i	safe handling of food
						44-45	2iii	habitats

WORK CARD 1 — Equipment

p.7 Tracing paper
p.10 Chair
p.14 Two stepladders and board or an adjustable ironing table
p.16 Computer workstation
p.18 Desk or work table

Assessment Activities

1. How do people's vital statistics compare? Try the experiment shown on p.9.
2. Display your results from Assessment Activity 1 by following the procedure on p.11.

WORK CARD 2 — Equipment

p.20 Spoons
p.23 Board, block, containers, protractor
p.24 Dumbbell
p.25 Two pairs of ladders, board, heavy bag
p.26 Books
p.29 Pole, bags

Assessment Activity

1. How high does a guard rail need to be for people in your class? Try the experiment on p.25 but also use p.14 to help you too.

WORK CARD 3 — Equipment

p.32 Box with lid and hooks, force meter
p.40 Camera
p.42 and p.44 Large pieces of paper, ruler

Assessment Activities

1. How does the force of opening a door vary? Perform the experiment on p.32 and plot a chart of your results.
2. Can you redesign a kitchen? Try the exercise on p.43.

WORK CARD 1

SCIENCE IN OUR WORLD WORK CARDS
How we vary

? Find out from Book 23: Science and Design

The number shown like this (p.00) tells you which page to find the answer.

1. State three ways in which people vary from each other. (p.6)
2. How do people's measurements change as they get older? (p.8)
3. What measurements of people sitting down might be used by designers? (p.8)
4. What is the shape of the chart produced when people are arranged into size groups? (p.11)
5. Why are toothbrushes usually available in only one size? (p.12)
6. What should be the height of a working surface? Which room in a home has most of these surfaces? (p.14)
7. What should you consider when sitting at a computer station. (p.16)
8. How should school desks be designed? (p.18)

✳ Show how . . .

1. the height of a working surface affects the way you can do things (p.15)
2. you can make an ergonome and use it to make a model seat (p.38 and p.39)

! Find out more

Look at these other Science in our world books for more information.

Book	*Page*	*Heading*
Growing and Changing	p.14	Racing growth
Presenting information	p.32	A column chart

SCIENCE IN OUR WORLD WORK CARDS
Forces and design

WORK CARD 2

? Find out from **Book 23: Science and design**

The number shown like this (p.00) tells you which page to find the answer.

1. What is the most important thing for a stable design? (p.20)
2. How do people balance the weight of an object as they pick it up? (p.21)
3. What is an important feature of a container? Why? (p.22)
4. What is the purpose of a guard rail? (p.25)
5. What are the natural levers of the body? (p.26)
6. Why can an adult hold books more easily than an eleven year old? (p.26)
7. What is a wrench used for? Why must it not be too long? (p.27)
8. How is muscle strain caused? (p.28)
9. Why is it better to use a suitcase with wheels than one without wheels? (p.28)

✳ Show how . . .

1. you can find the centre of gravity of different spoons. Which is easiest to use to take sand out of a tin? (p.20)
2. holding a weight can make you topple over more easily (p.24)

! Find out more

Look at these other Science in our world books for more information.

Book	Page	Heading
Falling	p.34	Staying upright
Starting and Stopping	p.12	Starting muscles

© 1993 ATLANTIC EUROPE PUBLISHING CO LTD

SCIENCE IN OUR WORLD WORK CARDS
Problems of design

WORK CARD 3

? Find out from **Book 23: Science and Design**

The number shown like this (p.00) tells you which page to find the answer.

1. What are the good and bad points of saucepan design? (p.30)
2. Where should a door knob be placed so that a door can be opened with the least force? (p.32 and p.33)
3. What happens to hand muscles as people get older? How does this affect them? (p.34)
4. Which kettle is better for old people to use? Why? (p.35)
5. Why are different materials used when a new product is being designed? (p.36 and p.37)
6. Why should things in a kitchen be conveniently placed? (p.40 and p.41)
7. What must you think about when planning a garden? (p.44)
8. Where is the best place for a garden pond be placed? Why? (p.44)
9. How should a garden be designed to attract birds? (p.45)

✳ Show how . . .

1. you would design a piece of the school grounds to make it more suitable for birdlife. Draw a large plan of your idea using p.45 to help you

! Find out more

Look at these other Science in our world books for more information.

Book	Page	Heading
How things work	p.32	Turn of the screw
Woodland life	p.26	Woodland and garden birds

© 1993 ATLANTIC EUROPE PUBLISHING CO LTD

WORK CARD 1			WORK CARD 2			WORK CARD 3		
Passing on information			**A human life begins**			**Breeding plants**		
Page	*AT/PoS*	*SoA/Key words*	*Page*	*AT/PoS*	*SoA/Key words*	*Page*	*AT/PoS*	*SoA/Key words*
10-14	2	5b	8-9, 22-23,			32-33	2	4a
18-21	2i	reproduction	25-29	2i	reproduction	34-39	2i	reproduction
30-31	2i	microbes						

Equipment

Equipment

Equipment

Assessment Activity

1. How easy is it to give clear instructions that give a reproducible result when tried by several people? Easy example – write down how you would make a simple meal. Mention every stage in its preparation. Harder example – explain how to tie a knot.

Assessment Activity

1. What dominant traits are passed through your family? Make a family tree from family photographs and say what dominant trait can be seen in each one.

Assessment Activities

1. How do plant seeds vary between species? Make a collection from fruit, garden plants and wild plants.
2. Can seeds of different plants be grown in the same conditions? Select five seeds from a number of different species and plant them in damp compost on a window sill.

 WORK CARD 1

SCIENCE IN OUR WORLD WORK CARDS
Passing on information

? Find out from **Book 24: Reproduction and Heredity**

The number shown like this (p.00) tells you which page to find the answer.

1. What are genes? (p.10)
2. Where are genes found? (p.10)
3. What do genes help to make? (p.11)
4. What are the two main parts of a cell? (p.14 and p.15)
5. What is a chromosome? Where are chromosomes found? (p.12)

6. What happens to the chromosomes when the cell divides? (p.19)
7. How are the chromosomes in the sex cells different from those in normal body cells? (p.20)
8. What are male and female sex cells called in animals and in plants? (p.21)
9. What kinds of tiny life forms can reproduce inside our bodies? (p.30)
10. Why are viruses difficult to control? (p.30)

✳ Show how . . .

1. a cell makes a copy of itself by making a flick book. Use the pictures on p.18 and p.19 to help.
2. a gene fits on a chromosome which fits inside a cell by making a cardboard model and taking it apart

❗ Find out more

Look at these other Science in our world *books for more information.*

Book	Page	Heading
Growing and Changing	p.44	Flowering and fruiting
Patterns and Shapes	p.44	Patterns of life

? Find out from Book 24: Reproduction and Heredity

The number shown like this (p.00) tells you which page to find the answer.

1. What is a trait? (p.8)
2. What is needed for fertilisation to take place? (p.22)
3. How can you tell a sperm cell from an egg cell? (p.22 and p.23)
4. What happens to a sperm cell during fertilisation? (p.22 and p.23)
5. What happens in the egg after fertilisation? (p.22 and p.23)
6. How do chemicals from the womb make the ball of cells grow a head and feet? (p.25)
7. What is the growing baby called? (p.25)
8. How are some throat cells different from nerve cells? (p.28 and p.29)
9. How does the embryo change from day 30 to 6 weeks? (p.6 and p.27)
10. How does the embryo change between 6 weeks and 9 months? (p.27)

✳ Show how . . .

1. you can tell that members of your family are related by displaying family photographs
2. a human embryo develops by making life-size cardboard models and explaining the changes that take place (p.26 and p.27)

! Find out more

Look at these other Science in our world books for more information.

Book	Page	Heading
Growing and Changing	p.6	In the beginning
Senses	p.12	Keeping in touch

© 1993 ATLANTIC EUROPE PUBLISHING CO LTD

? Find out from Book 24: Reproduction and Heredity

The number shown like this (p.00) tells you which page to find the answer.

1. What is pollen? What happens to it when it lands on the stigma of a flower? (p.32)
2. What are the three ways that pollen can reach a flower? (p.33)
3. What is a hybrid? Give some examples of hybrids. (p.34 and p.35)
4. What are the problems with some hybrids? (p.35)
5. How has the wheat plant been changed by farmers over the years? (p.36)
6. Which is the most commonly used food grain? (p.37)
7. Which crop plant may not survive in the wild? Why is this? (p.37)
8. What can be done with genes in biotechnology? (p.38)
9. How could biotechnology stop food from rotting? (p.39)

✳ Show how . . .

1. pollen on anthers can be seen in a flower. Show the position of the stigma and cut open an ovary to show the ovules (p.32)
2. plant breeders move pollen from one flower to another (p.33)

! Find out more

Look at these other Science in our world books for more information.

Book	Page	Heading
Woodland life	p.40	Blossom time
Measuring	p.44	Samples

© 1993 ATLANTIC EUROPE PUBLISHING CO LTD

WORK CARD 1			WORK CARD 2			WORK CARD 3		
The parts of a computer			Messages			Robots		
Page	*AT/PoS*	*SoA/Key words*	*Page*	*AT/PoS*	*SoA/Key words*	*Page*	*AT/PoS*	*SoA/Key words*
6-7,12-13	4i	control	8-11	4i	switches	32-33	4i	sensing
14-15	4i	switches	22-23	4i	control	34-35	4ii	forces
16-19	4i	logic gates	26-29	4i	sense and control	36	4i	control
20-21,						38-39	4i	sensing
30-31	4i	control				40-41	4ii	forces
						42	4iii	hydraulics

Equipment

Assessment Activity

Equipment

Assessment Activity

1. How accurately can you move a computer mouse?

Equipment

p.37 Remote grabber, remote controlled robot toy
p.42 Syringes, plastic tubes, T-piece
p.44 Battery, wires, motor, wheel and gears
p.45 Simple constructional materials

Assessment Activity

1. Can you make a robot hand? Perform the experiment on p.45

WORK CARD 1

SCIENCE IN OUR WORLD WORK CARDS

The parts of a computer

? Find out from Book 25: Computers and Robots

The number shown like this (p.00) tells you which page to find the answer.

1. Where does the computer store its information? (p.6)
2. What happens inside a computer when you switch it on? (p.7)
3. What is RAM and ROM? (p.13)
4. What kind of a device is a transistor? When was it discovered that it could be put on a silicon chip? (p.15)
5. What are gates and what do they do? (p.16)

6. What is an AND gate and how does it work? (p.18 and p.19)
7. Why do computers have their own clocks? How fast do they beat? (p.20)
8. Where in a computer is the Read Only Memory located? (p.21)
9. Where can computers be found in use around the home? (p.30 and p.31)

✳ Show how . . .

1. you can identify all the sockets on a computer and the peripherals that go into them. Explain what each of the peripherals does
2. you can use a computer to display experimental results

❗ Find out more

Look at these other *Science in our world books for more information.*

Book	Page	Heading
Senses	p.44	It's all in the mind
Patterns and Shapes	p.8	Patterns that mean yes or no

? Find out from **Book 25: Computers and Robots**

The number shown like this (p.00) tells you which page to find the answer.

1. What happens when you press a key down on a keyboard? (p.8 and p.9)
2. What is the mouse designed to do? (p.10)
3. What is an active button? (p.10)
4. What happens in the computer when an instruction is keyed in? (p.22)
5. How does a floppy disk differ from a hard disk? (p.24)
6. What is a computer that is used for writing letters called? (p.26)
7. How can computers help people avoid traffic jams? (p.28)
8. How does a computer control a car engine and brakes? (p.28)
9. How does a computer control a car radio? (p.28)
10. Which parts of a camera are controlled or monitored by a computer? (p.29)

✳ Show how . . .

1. you would store instructions on a floppy disk
2. you can use a mouse attached to a computer

❗ Find out more

Look at these other Science in our world *books for more information.*

Book	Page	Heading
Electricity and Magnetism	p.34	Magnets with a memory
Presenting information	p.28	Miniaturising information

© 1993 ATLANTIC EUROPE PUBLISHING CO LTD

? Find out from **Book 25: Computers and Robots**

The number shown like this (p.00) tells you which page to find the answer.

1. What is a robot? How is it different from an automated machine? (p.32)
2. Why don't robots look like humans? (p.34)
3. Why are robots useful in industry and in space exploration? (p.34)
4. How many motors are needed to control a robot's arm? In which directions can the arm move? (p.36)
5. How is a robot prevented from tipping over? (p.39)
6. What can be used to help a robot 'sense' its way along? (p.38 and p.39)
7. What does a robot need before it can look like a human body? (p.40)
8. Why are two-legged robots unlikely to be developed for many years? (p.41)
9. How can a liquid or a gas be used to operate a mechanism? (p.42)

✳ Show how . . .

1. messages travel from one part of a robot and back again by making a large diagram. Use the diagram on p.32 to help you
2. gears help to give greater control (p.44)

❗ Find out more

Look at these other Science in our world *books for more information.*

Book	Page	Heading
Electricity and Magnetism	p.32	Magnets on demand
Growing and Changing	p.18	Bones

© 1993 ATLANTIC EUROPE PUBLISHING CO LTD

WORK CARD 1

What are waves?

Page	AT/PoS	SoA/Key words
6	4	5f
9	4vi	how sounds change
10-11	4vi	how sounds change
12-13	4ii	Energy transfer
14-15	4	5f
16-21	4iv	sound reflection

Equipment

p.12 Balls, rainwater guttering, three billiard balls and a cue
p.17 Jar, cling film, castor sugar, tuning fork
p.18 Board, tuning fork, bridge support, pulley support, weight thread
p.19 Tuning fork, violin

Assessment Activities

1. How can you make the best standing wave? Find the places where the position of the block gives the best standing waves.

WORK CARD 2

Waves in water and on land

Page	AT/PoS	SoA/Key words
22-27	4ii	movement
28-29	4ii	energy transfer
40-41	4iii	forces
44-45	3i	materials

Equipment

p.22 Fish tank, water, flat stone or weight, polystyrene pieces or fishing floats; p.22 Long rope; p.24 Fish tank, water, fine sand, permanganate of potash, plunger; p.26 Fish tank, water, sand; p.27 Fine sand, large sheet of paper, hair drier, eye protection; p.28 Fish tank, plunger, heavy block, plastic slope, water; p.43 Jelly, board, wooden blocks, foam sheet

Assessment Activity

1. Which materials could be used to damp down jelly wobble? Repeat the experiment on p.43 with other materials instead of the foam sheet.

WORK CARD 3

Waves that travel through empty space

Page	AT/PoS	SoA/Key words
30-31	4iv	light, prisms
32-39	4ii	energy transfer

Equipment

p.30 Prism, card with slit, light from window, darkened room

Assessment Activity

1. How do the light waves in sunlight affect the colours in clothes and paper? Set out samples of different materials outside on sunny days. Look carefully for changes when compared with samples which are kept in the dark.

WORK CARD 1

SCIENCE IN OUR WORLD WORK CARDS
What are waves?

? Find out from Book 26: Waves and Vibrations

The number shown like this (p.00) tells you which page to find the answer.

1. What is a wave? What are the two main kinds of waves? (p.16)
2. What equipment enables us see some kinds of waves? (p.9)
3. what is the pitch and amplitude of a wave (p.11)
4. What do scientists call shock waves? (p.13)
5. What are sound waves? How do vocal chords produce them? (p.14)
6. Why do sounds get fainter? (p.14)
7. What happens when waves are reflected back into the path of oncoming waves? (p.16)
8. How does a tuning fork work? (p.18)
9. What are fundamentals and harmonics? How does the pattern of the harmonics affect an instrument? (p.21)
10. What is resonance? (p.46)

✳ Show how . . .

1. the vibrations of a tuning fork can make ripples in water by striking the fork and slowly dipping it into the water.
2. castor sugar is moved when a wave is reflected by performing the experiment p.17

! Find out more

Look at these other Science in our world books for more information.

Book	Page	Heading
Sounds and Music	p.6	What is sound?
Senses	p.22	Hearing clearly

❓ Find out from Book 26: Waves and Vibrations

The number shown like this (p.00) tells you which page to find the answer.

1. What happens when ripples pass through each other? (p.22)
2. What kind of wave moves through water? Which way do the individual water particles move? (p.24)
3. Which waves have most energy – small ones or large ones? (p.28)
4. What happens when a powerful wave reaches a beach and a cliff? (p.29)
5. What causes an earthquake? How many are there each year? (p.40)
6. How many tremors are produced in an earthquake? Which is the most destructive? (p.40 and p.41)
7. How can buildings be protected against earthquakes? (p.42 and p.43)

✳ Show how . . .

1. water moves when waves are formed (p.24 and p.25)
2. water can make sand form into ripples (p.26 and p.27)

❗ Find out more

Look at these other Science in our world *books for more information.*

Book	Page	Heading
How the Earth works	p.20	Earthquakes
The Earth in space	p.22	The Earth's tides

© 1993 ATLANTIC EUROPE PUBLISHING CO LTD

❓ Find out from Book 26: Waves and Vibrations

The number shown like this (p.00) tells you which page to find the answer.

1. What kinds of waves can travel through empty space? (p.30)
2. What happens to white light as it passes through a prism? (p.31)
3. What are the light detectors in our eyes called? (p.31)
4. What form of energy travels on infra-red waves? (p.32)
5. What can infra-red waves be used for? (p.32 and p.33)
6. What sort of waves are X-rays and ultraviolet rays? (p.34)
7. What are X-rays and ultraviolet light used for? (p.34 and p.35)
8. How are radio waves transmitted and received? (p.36)
9. What do the metal bars on an aerial do? (p.37)
10. Why are complicated circuits needed in radio sets? (p.38)

✳ Show how . . .

1. a prism can split up light by arranging a beam to strike its surface in a darkened room
2. you can set up the aerial on a portable radio to receive a very clear radio programme

❗ Find out more

Look at these other Science in our world *books for more information.*

Book	Page	Heading
Light	p.6	Sunlight
The Earth in Space	p.10	The atmosphere

© 1993 ATLANTIC EUROPE PUBLISHING CO LTD

WORK CARD 1	WORK CARD 2	WORK CARD 3
Energy on the move	Conserving energy in the home	Energy saving round the world

Page	AT/PoS	SoA/Key words	Page	AT/PoS	SoA/Key words	Page	AT/PoS	SoA/Key words
10-15	4ii	energy transfers	8,20-21,23,			24-25,		
17,42-43	4ii	implications of energy resources	26-28,30-31	4ii	implications of energy resources	32-38	4ii	implications of energy resources
44-45	4	5c						

Equipment

p.11 Radiometer
p.13 Kitchen foil, stiff metal wire, short wires with eyes, lard, heavy support, camping stove.

Assessment Activity

1. Do different metals conduct heat in the same way? Use stiff wires of different metals to compare their speed of conduction. (p13)

Equipment

p.28 Foam sheet, polyester and fibres, black cotton, white cotton, black plastic, white plastic, aluminium foil, wrapping paper, jug, water thermometer

Assessment Activity

1. Which is the best heat insulator to keep a jug of water warm? Using several identical jugs, thermometers and a range of materials, try the experiment on p.28 and p.29.

Equipment

Assessment Activity

1. Does the colour of the glass jar over seeds affect the way the seeds grow? Paint jars different colours and place them over pots of germinating seedlings.

 WORK CARD 1

SCIENCE IN OUR WORLD WORK CARDS
Energy on the move

❓ Find out from **Book 27: Don't waste energy**

The number shown like this (p.00) tells you which page to find the answer.

1. What is heat radiation? (p.10)
2. How does the Earth receive its energy? (p.10)
3. When can objects conduct heat? (p.12)
4. How is conduction used to heat food, cool down engines and release waste heat from power stations? (p.12)
5. What is convection? How does it help to heat a room, cool a drink, cook food and keep tropical fish warm? (p.14 and p.15)

6. How can we save energy used in transport? (p.17)
7. How can people travel in cities and use less energy? (p.42)
8. Why are ships and barges energy efficient? (p.43)
9. Which five countries have the greatest reserves of fossil fuels? Which five countries are the greatest consumers of energy? (p.44 and p.45)

✳ Show how . . .

1. a candle gives out two forms of energy. Make some equipment that can be used to raise the temperature of water (p.6)
2. heat moves along a wire by performing the experiment on p.13. You must ask your teacher to help you heat the wire

❗ Find out more

Look at these other Science in our world books for more information.

Book	Page	Heading
Water	p.44	Steam driven
Energy	p.40	Transporting energy

? Find out from Book 27: Don't waste energy

The number shown like this (p.00) tells you which page to find the answer.

1. When are the peaks of energy use in the home? (p.8 and p.9)
2. Which parts of a home lose energy? How much energy does each part lose? (p.20 and p.21)
3. How can a home be made to save more energy? (p.20 and p.21)
4. Arrange the energy saving methods in order, starting with the one that returns its cost the quickest. (p.20 and p.21)

5. Explain why are insulated floor coverings are important. (p.23)
7. Why is a vacuum flask a most efficient energy saver? (p.27)
8. How can hot liquid insulators be made more attractive to use? (p.28)
9. What two ways are used to make a kettle more energy efficient? (p.30)

✳ Show how . . .

1. a joss stick can be used to demonstrate how air moves about in a room. (You must ask a teacher to help you with the joss stick.)
2. the air temperature varies at different places in the school over a few days. Explain why you think the air temperature varies

! Find out more

Look at these other Science in our world books for more information.

Book	Page	Heading
Light	p.8	Artificial light
Energy	p.42	Conserving home energy

© 1993 ATLANTIC EUROPE PUBLISHING CO LTD

? Find out from Book 27: Don't waste energy

The number shown like this (p.00) tells you which page to find the answer.

1. How can Spanish apartments and Swiss farmhouses be built to save energy? (p.24)
2. How do glass houses make use of the Sun's energy? (p.24)
3. How were homes built in New Orleans before air-conditioning was invented? (p.25)
4. How do old English stone houses save energy? (p.25)

5. Why does a pressure cooker use less energy to cook food than an ordinary pan? (p.33)
6. What do people in developing countries use as a source of energy? How is this energy wasted? (p.34)
7. What can be done to help solve the energy problem in developing countries? (p.35)
8. Why does recycling save energy? How have steelworks cut their energy costs? (p.38)

✳ Show how . . .

1. a glass jar over a plant pot of germinating seeds helps them to grow faster than seeds in a pot without a jar
2. energy can be saved in a house by building a model house with energy saving features (p.20, p.21, p.24 and p.25)

! Find out more

Look at these other Science in our world books for more information.

Book	Page	Heading
Falling	p.26	Falling water
Energy	p.28	Energy for all

© 1993 ATLANTIC EUROPE PUBLISHING CO LTD

REFERENCE CARD

WORK CARD 1			WORK CARD 2			WORK CARD 3		
A range of materials			Properties of materials			Comparing materials		
Page	*AT/PoS*	*SoA/Key words*	*Page*	*AT/PoS*	*SoA/Key words*	*Page*	*AT/PoS*	*SoA/Key words*
7-9	3	3b(part)	14,16	4	3c	28-30	3i	properties
10-11,13,			20	3iii	action of heat	32-33,		
42-43	3i	properties	23	4i	components	36-37	3	5c (part)
44-45	2iii	human activities	24-25	3i	hardness	38-39,41	3i	properties
			26	3	4a			

Equipment

p.42 Straws, scissors, wet pottery clay, board, roller

Assessment Activity

1. How does straw in clay alter the clay's properties? Follow the instructions on p.42 then test for hardness, flexibility and strength.

Equipment

p.15 Pasta machine
p.16 Food mixer, cornflour and water
p.17 Jelly, baseboard, scale pan and weighs, ruler
p.24 Copper coin, knife, glazed wall tile, piece of plastic, wood and paper

Assessment Activities

1. How does a jelly change as it is pressed down? Set up the experiment shown on p.17. Repeat the experiment with crustless bread and compare the results.
2. Which spoon conducts heat best? Put a selection of spoons in hot water and add a piece of butter to the end of each handle. Record the order of melting and write down ways of improving the test.

Equipment

p.30 Sealing wax
p.37 Twelve nails, three jars, airing cupboard or equivalent warm place, distilled water
p.38 Clay

Assessment Activities

1. How does clay change after firing? Work out some strength, hardness, compressibility and flexibility tests for unfired and fired clay blocks and compare the results.
2. Compare strips of metal for flexibility, strength and hardness. (Eye protection should be worn in all tests.)

WORK CARD 1

SCIENCE IN OUR WORLD WORK CARDS
A range of materials

? Find out from **Book 28: Materials**

The number shown like this (p.00) tells you which page to find the answer.

1. What are plant fibres used for? (p.7)
2. What can the sap of some plants produce? (p.7)
3. What are organic materials? (p.8)
4. What materials can we get from rocks? (p.8 and p.9)
5. What are the materials in an electrical cable? How is each one used? (p.10)
6. What properties does a plastic bottle need to hold a fizzy drink? (p.11)
7. What materials have replaced stone to make large buildings? (p.13)
8. What is a composite and what is a laminate? Give an example of each. (p.42 and p.43)
9. What damage can be done to the natural world when materials are collected or produced? (p.44)

✳ Show how . . .

1. a chair, a toy or an old hard-backed book is made from a range of materials
2. you would use a range of materials to make a hand-held windmill

❗ Find out more

Look at these other Science in our world books for more information.

Book	Page	Heading
Fibres	p.20	Secrets of paper
Don't throw it away	p.22	Let's give a hand

? Find out from Book 28: Materials

The number shown like this (p.00) tells you which page to find the answer.

1. What three changes can take place in a material when a force is applied to it? (p.14)
2. What happens to some liquids when they are stirred? Give examples. (p.16)
3. How do materials change when they are heated? (p.20)
4. What happens to the liquid in a thermometer when it warms up and then cools down? (p.20)
5. Name a good conductor of heat. What could it be used for? (p.21)
6. What can and poor conductors be used for? (p.21)
7. Name a good conductor and a good insulator of electricity. What are they used for on a circuit board? (p.23)
9. Why must scissors and dentist's drills be very hard? (p.25)

✳ Show how . . .

1. clear plastics have stress patterns (p.18)
2. you can test materials for hardness (p.24)

❗ Find out more

Look at these other Science in our world books for more information.

Book	Page	Heading
Electricity and Magnetism	p.12	Conductors and insulators
Don't waste energy	p.22	Room to experiment

© 1993 ATLANTIC EUROPE PUBLISHING CO LTD

? Find out from Book 28: Materials

The number shown like this (p.00) tells you which page to find the answer.

1. What is the proper name for plastics? (p.28)
2. Name four useful properties of polymers. Give examples of how they are used. (p.29)
3. What are the two main types of plastic? How do they differ? (p.30)
4. Which metals are ferrous metals? Which are non-ferrous? (p.32)
5. Name four ways in which metals are shaped. Give examples of how each shape is used. (p.32 and p.33)
6. What is corrosion? How can the hulls of steel ships be protected from it? (p.36)
7. What is a ceramic? Name some common examples. (p.38 and p.39)
8. What happens to a ceramic when it is heated to a high temperature? (p.39)
9. How is common glass made? (p.40)

✳ Show how . . .

1. a thermoplastic can be shaped by using sealing wax (p.30)
2. rust occurs on steel nails by performing the experiment on p.37. Explain and demonstrate your results to the rest of the class

❗ Find out more

Look at these other Science in our world books for more information.

Book	Page	Heading
Don't throw it away	p.30	Steel appeal
Patterns and Shapes	p.42	Making new materials

© 1993 ATLANTIC EUROPE PUBLISHING CO LTD

WORK CARD 1			WORK CARD 2			WORK CARD 3		
Communicating			Vision			Showing information		
Page	*AT/PoS*	*SoA/Key words*	*Page*	*AT/PoS*	*SoA/Key words*	*Page*	*AT/PoS*	*SoA/Key words*
6-11, 20-21	2i	behaviour	12-19, 22-25	2i	behaviour	30-45	1	recording data

Work Card 1

Equipment
p.10 Coloured flags

Assessment Activity
1. Can you send a semaphore message? Use coloured flags and the information on p.10 and p.11 to help you. Ask someone at a distance from you to write down the message they receive. Does it match the message that you thought you sent?

Work Card 2

Equipment
p.17 Paper, coloured pens and pencils, ruler
p.18 Tracing paper, white paper, pencil, ruler
p.22 and p.27 Cardboard, coloured pens and pencils, ruler

Assessment Activities
1. Can a wrapper make an object look bigger or smaller? (p.17)
2. Can you design a logo scientifically? (p.27)

Work Card 3

Equipment
p.32 to p.34, p.38 and p.39 Graph paper

Assessment Activities
1. Can you make the calculations for a pie chart? Try the exercise on p.36 and p.37.
2. Plot a line chart of your pulse rate. Take your pulse for 15 seconds and multiply your answer by four to obtain a beats per minute value. Take your pulse every five minutes for half an hour as you do your schoolwork and make a line graph of your results.

WORK CARD 1
SCIENCE IN OUR WORLD WORK CARDS
Communicating

? Find out from Book 29: Presenting information

The number shown like this (p.00) tells you which page to find the answer.

1. What does 'communication' mean? Give three examples. (p.6)
2. Name the seven stages of communication. (p.6 and p.7)
3. How is the picture that you see with your eyes built up in your brain? (p.9)
4. How did people send signals to one another in the past? (p.10)
5. What is semaphore? When do ship navigators use it? (p.11)
6. Spell your name in semaphore pictures. (p.10 and p.11)
7. How do people who are hard of hearing receive information? (p.11)
8. What is the most easily understood international sign? (p.20)
9. Why is it important to have symbols on information signs as well as words? (p.20 and p.21)

✳ Show how . . .

1. you can communicate an idea just by mime (p.9)
2. finger spelling can be used to send a message (p.10 and p.11)

! Find out more

Look at these other Science in our world *books for more information.*

Book	Page	Heading
Sounds and Music	p.8	Sounds that signal
Senses	p.8	What is that smell?

WORK CARD 2

Vision

? Find out from Book 29: Presenting information

The number shown like this (p.00) tells you which page to find the answer.

1. What is the field of view? What is its most important region? (p.12)
2. Which things are truly in focus when we look at them? (p.13)
3. Why are symbols used instead of many words for some road signs? (p.13)
4. How are traffic signals and road signs designed to help colour-blind people? (p.15)
5. What is an optical illusion? Where are they used? (p.17)
6. What is perspective? How do close and distant objects appear to the eye? (p.18)
7. What does the lens do to objects that the eye looks at? (p.22 and p.23)
8. What are two common eye problems? How are they caused? (p.24)
9. Name four problems that older people have with vision. How can they be remedied? (p.25)

✳ Show how . . .

1. the edges of objects have a common vanishing point (p.18 and p.19)
2. you would make a sign for a railway station (p.22)

! Find out more

Look at these other Science in our world books for more information.

Book	Page	Heading
Light	p.32	The world turned upside down
Senses	p.32	Get the picture

© 1993 ATLANTIC EUROPE PUBLISHING CO LTD

WORK CARD 3

Showing information

? Find out from Book 29: Presenting information

The number shown like this (p.00) tells you which page to find the answer.

1. When presenting the results from an investigation, what three things should you consider? (p.30)
2. What are measurements called and how are charts useful? (p.31)
3. What are axes? How are they arranged on a chart? (p.31)
4. What are the stages in making a column chart? (p.32 and p.33)
5. How does a bar chart differ from a column chart? (p.32 and p.35)
6. When would you make a pie chart of your results? (p.36 and p.37)
7. What are the stages in making a line chart? (p.38 and p.39)
8. How can changing the scales of axes make one set of results look like two completely different charts? (p.40 and p.41)
9. When is a flow chart useful? Give three examples? (p.42 and p.43)

✳ Show how . . .

1. you can display the heights of people in your class by making a large, accurate and attractive column chart. (p.32 and p.33)
2. the distances travelled by toy cars after they leave a ramp can be displayed as a bar chart (p.34 and p.35)

! Find out more

Look at these other Science in our world books for more information.

Book	Page	Heading
Falling	p.20	Stretching
Measuring	p.32	Temperature

© 1993 ATLANTIC EUROPE PUBLISHING CO LTD

Glossary

abseil

is used by people when they want to get down a cliff very quickly. They make a series of jumps down the cliff, using the rope to support their weight. It is very important to use a rope with just the right amount of stretch or the rope might break

absorb

to soak up

>**shocks**: rubber is an example of a material that changes shape and absorbs pulls and pushes

>**sound**: some of the best absorbing materials are those with rough surfaces or those with holes

>**gas or a liquid**: many powders absorb water when they are left open and this causes them to swell

>**radiation**: the process of soaking up energy that has been received by radiation, often sunlight

acceleration

the increase in speed of an object. Acceleration is sometimes measured in the time it takes to reach a certain speed from a standing start. It is usually measured in metres per second per second. For an object falling under gravity the acceleration is 9.8 metres per second per second. Deceleration is the opposite of acceleration, that is the rate of slowing down of an object.

acid

any substance that dissolves in water and which corrodes anything it touches

acid rain

when fossil fuels such as coal, oil and gas are burned in power stations and in car engines large amounts of a gas called sulphur dioxide are produced. This gas drifts up into the air and mixes with water droplets in the clouds. The raindrops that fall are acid. Acid rain can kill trees and the fish in lakes and rivers

adhesive

a material, often known as 'glue' which can be used to join other materials together

aerosol

an aerosol is a mixture of small particles, such as water or paint droplets, suspended in a gas such as air. In a spray can the liquid that is to be made into particles is held under pressure with a gas. In the past the gases used were called CFCs. These gases are known to damage the environment.

Aerosol cans now have different gases in them, but a hand cranked spray will do many of the jobs that a pressure can will do and it does no damage to the environment because it uses air to force the liquid through the nozzle

ailerons

in aeroplanes these are the flaps that can be lifted from the trailing side of the main wings. They are the flaps you see in use if you travel by air and look from the cabin windows. Pilots use them for changing direction and also for slowing the plane as it comes in to land

air-conditioning

the process of controlling the temperature (and often the moisture content) of the air in a room in order to make it more pleasant to live in. Air-conditioning units can be thought of as a combination of a giant refrigerator and a heater. Which one is used at any time depends on whether the room is too hot or too cold for comfort

algae

tiny plants which grow together and make bright green, powdery patches

alkali

any substance that dissolves in water and which is a derived from a mineral salt

alternating current

mains electricity is sent along cables as an alternating current with a frequency of 50 Hertz in some countries and 60 Hertz in others. Because the human ear can detect this frequency, you can sometimes 'hear' electricity moving in the wires strung between pylons or when near to electricity stations. It sounds like a hum

amplifier

something which makes sounds louder

amplitude

the amplitude of a wave is the distance between a crest and a trough. In sound waves larger amplitudes give louder sounds. Loudness is measured in decibels

annual

a plant that grows, flowers, sets seed and dies in a year

antenna

>**computer:** a rod-like sensing device. In the case of a robot, an antenna may give important information about the environment it touches

>**insect:** the main sensing organ of an insect. There are usually one or two pairs of antennae attached to the animal's head and they contain the receptors for sound, smell, touch and temperature

appliance

the name given to any electrical equipment used in the home that is used to make housework easier or to make living more comfortable, for example a washing machine or a stove. It could also mean a radio or TV

aquaplaning

the tendency for a thin film of water to develop when a vehicle moves at high speed on a wet road. The purpose of the pattern of deep cuts, or tread, on a tyre is to prevent aquaplaning and loss of control

arc
a small segment of a circle.
A quarter of a circle has an arc
of 90° for example

argon
argon is a gas that makes up about
one per cent of the air. It is called an
inert gas, which means that it will
not react with other substances
easily. Argon is used in light bulbs
or fluorescent lamps because it will
not burn up when hot

arteries
the major blood vessels in the body

astronomy
the science of studying the
Universe. Astronomers are
concerned with the nature and
origins of the Universe, including
the Earth, but they do not study the
Earth in detail

atmosphere
the shell of gases that surrounds the
Earth. There are several layers to
the atmosphere, the one closest to
the ground, called the troposphere,
contains mostly nitrogen gas but
also includes enough oxygen for us
to breath and water vapour that
provide the moisture for clouds.
It also holds carbon dioxide gas
(see Greenhouse Effect) and large
amounts of dust and other tiny
particles that have been swept off
the land by winds. The circulation
of air in the troposphere gives rise
to weather patterns; above it is the
stratosphere, the region of thin
air containing the gas ozone that
helps to shield animals and plants
from too high levels of ultra-violet
radiation

atom
the smallest particle that makes
up one of the 92 pure stable
substances, or elements, in the
Universe. An atom consists of a
nucleus in which there are protons
and neutrons, and a set of electrons
which surround it. Atoms are too
small to be seen even with the most
powerful microscope

autogyro
a machine that has freely spinning
rotor blades. It is driven forward by
a propeller. The forward movement
of the machine causes the rotor
blades to turn and this gives lift.
It is not as manoeuvrable as a
helicopter

automatic/automated
a machine that works automatically
is able to perform a certain task
independently. An automated
system is one where a set of
machines do a number of tasks
automatically, one perhaps feeding
material to another

avalanche
the rapid movement of a huge mass
of snow down a mountainside.
Avalanches can reach speeds of
hundreds of kilometres an hour
and they can cause great damage to
any buildings that lie in their paths

average
the word used to describe a value
that is thought to be the most
common. The average is calculated,
for example, by adding all the
heights of a group together and
then dividing by the number in the
group. This is called the mean value
by mathematicians

axis (axes)
geometry: an axis is the line
around which a body spins.
For example the axis around
which a wheel spins is called
the hub.
planets: all planets spin and
so they can be thought of as
having an axis through the line
which is at the centre of the
spin. The Earth, like every
other body, spins in space
around an imaginary spindle
that goes through the North
and South Poles and it is at an
angle of 23.5 degrees to its orbit
chart: when drawing a chart
the horizontal and vertical
reference lines are called axes.
The place where the axes join
is called the origin of the axes
and its value is usually zero.
Scales are marked along each
axis from the origin

bacteria
microscopic organisms which are
neither plant nor animal. Many
kinds feed on the dead bodies
of plants and animals. In even a
handful of woodland soil there
would be many millions of bacteria,
all doing the useful job of helping
to decompose dead material. As
they do this they release gases

bagpipes
a musical reed instrument that
is pumped with air supplied from
an animal bladder

balding
the gradual loss of hair from the
head because the hair producing
cells in the scalp begin to die. It is
a common feature of men, but very
rare in women

barometer
an instrument for measuring
the pressure of the air in the
atmosphere. High pressure spells
fine weather, low pressure forecasts
rain, very low pressure tells of an
approaching storm

bearing
a support for a moving part. The
hub of a bicycle wheel contains a
bearing. This allows the wheel to
turn easily on the shaft

beat
a sound made regularly. The beat
helps to maintain the rhythm and
keeps the musical time

behaviour
the way people act. Behaviour
normally refers to the normal day
to day activities of people, but
sometimes design has to take into
account the behaviour of people in
emergency situations such as a fire

Big Bang
the theory known as the Big Bang
assumes that the Universe started
from a single point, 15 - 30 billion
years ago, and that since this first
time everything has been travelling
outwards, like the pieces thrown
out by some immense explosion

binary
the system of numbers which uses only combinations of 1 and 0 to describe all numbers. In this system, for example, the combination 10 (1 and 0) is 2. This system is particularly important in computing because 1 can be represented by a switch set to 'on' and 0 can be represented by a switch set to 'off'

bituminous
a word used to describe the character of soft black coal which burns with a smoky yellow flame

blizzard
a snowstorm with very strong winds. In a blizzard it is almost impossible to see ahead because of the driving snow

blood vessels
the tubes that carry blood from the heart to the rest of the body and back again. Blood is red when it has plenty of oxygen

blueprint
in engineering a blueprint is an original plan or model that plays a major role in influencing the design of the finished product. Biologists borrowed the name to make it easier for people to visualise the role of the gene pattern in life

bow (musical)
an instrument used for making strings vibrate. Bows only work if they are coated with rosin and make rapid juddering movements

brass (musical)
musical instruments played by the mouth using the lips as a reed

breeze
a gentle movement of air too light to rustle the pages of an open book

bricks
a special form of clay building block found widely in the world. Some bricks have specially shaped dents in their faces to take cement, others have plain faces. Bricks are about a quarter the size of concrete building blocks

brittle
the state of a material such that it is liable to break (fracture) when stressed

bugle
a kind of simple horn designed for playing military tunes

calibrate
to compare a measuring instrument with known standards so that it can be reliably used

camber
the slightly arched surface of a road which is designed to provide a slope for water to run off the road during a rainstorm. On curves cambers are often designed with a single slope from the outside towards the inside. This is called banking

camouflage
a pattern of colours designed to blend in with the surroundings. Most types of camouflage involve patterns of colours, such as stripes or blotches

> **animals**: any way in which an animal makes itself difficult to be seen. Many animals have colours which let their body blend in with their surroundings. Green is a useful camouflage colour for a caterpillar on a young leaf; speckled brown will camouflage an insect on the bark of a tree

canopy
the part of the wood above your head which is made by the interlocking branches of trees that are growing close together

capacity
the amount of volume that can be contained in a vessel when filled to the brim or to some other maximum mark made on its side

carbohydrate
a group of substances that includes a number of sugar-making chemicals, of which the most important is starch

carbon
one of the basic elements, or basic substances, which are the building blocks of everything in the Universe. Carbon is an essential element for life. Of the 11 billion substances known, 10 billion of them contain carbon

carding
the process which gets the natural fibres pulled out into line, removes the seeds and other small pieces of unwanted material

carnivore
an animal that eats mainly meat. Animals such as tigers, bears, or foxes are large carnivores, but a centipede, which eats other insects, is also a carnivore

cartilage
the rubbery layer of tissue - often known as gristle - that grows between moving bones and which acts as a combined bearing and shock-absorber

cell

> **living**: the simplest form of independent life. Our bodies are made of millions of these small building blocks called cells. It consists of a nucleus containing the genes which act as the blueprint for future generations surrounded by the parts of a cell that provide it with nourishment and energy and allow it to live an independent life. The simplest organisms, such as bacteria, are each made of a single cell. Cells have evolved to perform many special functions, such as turning food into energy, or receiving signals about the outside world. Our bodies are constantly making new cells to replace the dead ones. Human bodies contain about 50 trillion cells

> **shape**: a closed shape that packs together with other similar shapes to form a pattern. In a honeycomb made by bees each cell is made of wax and is occupied by an egg

cellulose
a natural material that makes up the bulk of plant tissues. Cellulose often forms into tiny strings, or fibres

centre of gravity
it is often useful to try to work out the place where the real weight of an object acts. The term centre of gravity is used to describe this place. If the object has most of its weight high up, it is probably 'top heavy': that is, it has its centre of gravity high up. If the weight is mostly low down, it is 'bottom heavy' with a centre of gravity low down. This position makes an object much less likely to fall over

centrifugal force
when an object whirls round and round it always tries to fly outwards and away from its orbit. Many people call the effect the centrifugal force

ceramic
a special kind of clay that has been baked hard. Most kitchen tiles are ceramic. They are hard and brittle, but they can stand up to great heat and they are therefore useful in a space craft when it flies back through the Earth's atmosphere

chaos
a form of disorder. People describe something as chaotic when they can recognise no pattern to it, yet mathematicians have recently begun to understand that what seems without pattern may actually be following some very simple rules

charge
the amount of stored electrical energy present. People often speak of 'charging a battery'. What they mean is that they must replace the electrical energy that has been used. To do this they use a piece of equipment called a 'charger'

chip
the general term to describe an integrated circuit etched on to the surface of a thin piece of silicon

chlorophyll
the green pigment in plant cells that can absorb the energy in sunshine and use it to help the plant create new tissue

chord
the effect you get when you play three or more notes at the same time

chrysalis
the silken case made by a caterpillar as it prepares to turn into a butterfly

circuit
a circuit is made of a number of electrical devices connected up in such a way that electricity flows through them. A circuit can be simple, as in the case of a torch, where a battery and a bulb are connected through a switch, or it might be very complicated, such as in a computer where tens of thousands of connections are involved

cirrus
a wispy form of cloud that forms in a clear sky. Cirrus cloud is very high in the sky and made entirely of ice crystals

clay
the finest size of rock flour produced when rocks are broken down by the action of the weather. Clay is too small to be seen piece by piece. When moist, clay feels sticky

climate
the pattern of weather that happens on average at any place. Climates are described in terms of average rainfall, snowfall, temperature and the like. Patterns of natural vegetation often closely correspond with climate zones because plants are sensitive to long term weather patterns rather than day to day changes

cloud
water droplets or ice crystals that form in the air above the ground

cloven
a name used to describe the hooves of deer which are slit into two

cocktail
a mixture of a range of different liquids

cocoon
the silken wrapping or case made by a caterpillar as it prepares to turn into a moth. The silkworm gradually wraps itself in silk by pushing out a long continuous thread from a special place on its body

colonise
to become established in a new area. In places where there is severe competition, the most successful colonist is often the plant that can reproduce fastest

colour blindness
a term which refers to the difficulty some people have in recognising certain colours, especially red, blue-violet or green. Colour blindness is an inherited disorder and it is mostly found in males

combustible
a material that can burn is said to be combustible. Three conditions are needed for combustion: the material, a source of heating such as a match, and a supply of air

communicate
the many ways in which meaning is sent or understood from some information. The word is used in many ways: it is used to describe a conversation between people; exchanging data between computers; and the courting actions of animals

component
a small piece of a complex device such as a computer. A component will perform just one function, and a designer uses many kinds of component so that, when they are put together, they can perform many complex tasks. Electrical components include resistors, capacitors and chips; mechanical components include gear, rods and pivots

compound
a substance that it made from two or more elements bonded together.

compress
to make smaller by applying a
force. Most frequently a force is
applied in just one direction so that
compression results in squashing in
the direction of the force. Often this
is balanced by expansion, for
example, as dough is rolled out
by a pastry roller

compromise
to take a view about something
which is perhaps slightly less than
ideal from any one point of view,
but which, on balance, gets closest
to meeting all the competing points
of view

computer
a machine for processing
information at high speed.
The principle of sending simple
commands was invented by Henry
Babbage in the 19th century, but
high speed computing became
possible only after the invention
of the transistor in the 1950s.
Computers use patterns of binary
numbers as instructions

concave
the way a surface is dished so that
it faces inwards. Typical concave
objects include the inside of a spoon
and the inside of a cupped hand

condensation
the formation of water droplets
on a cold surface

conduct
the way some materials can transfer
electricity or heat. For example,
heat will flow (be conducted) from
the warmer body (which has the
greater energy) to the cooler one
until the temperatures become the
same. Materials which do not easily
act as conductors are called
insulators

cone
a shape with a circular base and
sloping sides that meet at a point.
A wizard's hat is often shown in
books as a tall cone

conserve
to protect and use wisely so that
the resource will not be exhausted.
Conserving the use of fossil fuels is

one of the most important tasks
facing the world today

continental plate
one of the large slabs of the Earth's
crust that carries one of the world's
five continents. Plates are hundreds
of kilometres thick and are moved
very slowly by forces deep within
the Earth. When two slabs meet one
is forced under the other in a series
of sharp jerking movements. Each
movement gives rise to an
earthquake

controller
a device that enables an operator to
control a robot or other automated
equipment. The controller is often
a set of switches that control each
movement of a robot

convection
this is a natural process of
circulating heat through liquids
and gases It happens because warm
liquids and gases become lighter
and rise, while cool ones become
denser and sink. If a gas is made
warmer it becomes lighter and
starts to rise. If it gets cooler it
becomes heavier and sinks. Air in
contact with a heater rises as it
warms. New air flows in to take its
place and is warmed in turn. This
sets up a flow of air or a current

    Earth: this is the process
    whereby liquids turn over and
    over when heated from below.
    Convection is thought to
    happen in the Earth's mantle,
    and it is responsible for the
    movement of the continents
    atmosphere: on Earth the
    tropics are places where air
    and ocean heat most strongly
    and the poles are places where
    there is the greatest cooling

convex
the way a surface is bulged out so
that it faces outwards. The outside
of a ball is a convex surface

co-ordinates
a system of describing the position
of an object. The edge of a map, for
example, is marked off in numbers
which can then be used to describe

the location of any feature. On the
Earth the co-ordinates are longitude
and latitude. A location might then
be given as, for example, 45° W and
24° S (which is Sao Paulo in Brazil)

co-ordination
the process of doing many
linked things at the same time.
For example, when we walk we
normally co-ordinate the movement
of our arms and legs to keep our
bodies balanced

corrode
the process where the elements of
the weather or water begin to act
chemically on a metal or other
material so that its surface becomes
pitted and it loses its strength

corrugation
a surface that is shaped into long
lines of wrinkles. Corrugations are
often added to materials to make
them stronger. Sheets of wrapping
paper and sheets of steel (intended
for use as roofing) are common
examples

counterbalance
if an object is balanced it
will have the same weight on
both sides of the pivoting point.
A counterbalance is a weight that
is added to something to get it into
balance. Counterbalances are used
in many places. They can be found
as a weight on the end of a bar,
or a weight on the end of a pulley

crystal
a mineral that has developed with
regular faces

cumulonimbus
tall rain-bearing thunderclouds

cumulus clouds
pillow-like clouds that can give
showery weather

cyclone
a name given to a tropical storm
with severe winds

cylinder
a solid shape with a circular plan.
Rods, columns and trees are all
examples of cylinders. A hollow
cylinder is called a tube

data
a series of observations or measurements that have been collected as part of an experiment or investigation. Another common word for data is information

deceleration
the reduction in speed of an object. Like acceleration, it is measured in metres per second per second

decibel
a unit that gives a measure of the loudness of a sound

deciduous
when plants shed their leaves for part of the year and stop growing they are said to be deciduous. Many trees are deciduous to allow them to survive a harsh winter or a drought

decomposers
living things such as bacteria, fungi and earthworms which feed on the dead bodies of plants and animals and break them down, releasing materials that can be directly used as food by growing plants

deform
to change shape. Materials may deform permanently or they may go back to their original shape if the force is removed or sometimes if they are heated

designer
a person who works out the shape and structure of something using sketches, computers and other aids

detergent
a chemical that acts on surface grease to remove it. Many detergents are made of lots of chemicals that can dissolve most forms of dirt and grease

developing world
those countries in which the majority of people have yet to develop a standard of living similar to that of industrial countries

dew
condensation that forms on leaves and other surfaces overnight

diet
the types of food we eat. When people speak of 'going on a diet', they usually mean they are going to change their diet to one with less energy in it

digestion
the way in which the body breaks down the food into useful chemicals

dilate
a word that means to make larger. The pupil in the eye gets larger, or dilates, under dark conditions. This is done to capture the greatest amount of light possible and help an animal to see better

dimensions
a measurement of the size of something in a particular direction such as width or height. In science, the fundamental dimensions are mass, length and time

dimmer
a piece of electrical equipment that cuts down the voltage that reaches a light bulb. With less voltage (pressure) the bulb then glows less brightly and uses less electric current

diode
a simple electronic device that allows an electric current to flow in only one direction. Some diodes can emit a beam of light when an electric current is passed through them

disposable
an object or appliance that cannot be repaired once it has worn out or become broken. Many of the components of electronic machines such as computers use disposable parts, but most ball point pens cannot be refilled and these are therefore also disposable

dissolve
the way in which a solid is absorbed by a liquid. Water can dissolve more substances than any other liquid. Many substances are colourless when they have dissolved in water

smell: many small particles, or molecules, are in the air as it is breathed into the nose. As they dissolve in the mucus of the nose the particles cause a chemical change and this sends signals to the brain

distilled water
water that has been boiled and then allowed to condense. Distilled water is free of the natural impurities that are found in tap or stream waters

DNA
Deoxyribonucleic acid (DNA) and ribonucleic acid (RNA) are the two chemical substances used to transfer information about heredity from parent to offspring. They are called nucleic acids because they are found in the core, or nucleus, of each cell

down (bird)
the very soft underfeathers of a bird. Chicks start life covered with down, but as they grow older the larger body and flight feathers grow through the down and hide it

drizzle
a form of light rain with small drops

drought
a period which is dry for longer than usual and when people, plants or animals start to suffer

drum
a sound box with a skin stretched across it. It is hit with the hand or sticks

dune
an undulating shape of sand in a desert. Sand dunes are produced as wind blows over the land in a regular way, picking sand from some places and depositing it again in others

dye
a staining or colouring chemical. Natural dyes have been used for thousands of years, but it is difficult to get a complete range of colours. Artificial, or synthetic, dyes are often made from oil

ear muffs
special 'headphones' that have sound deadening material inside each ear cup

eardrum
the flap of skin inside the ear that acts as a sounding board for vibrations in the air. As sound waves make it vibrate, so the bones inside the ear are also made to vibrate, thereby passing on the sound. The eardrum also serves as a door in the ear, keeping out dirt and liquids

earthquake
violent shaking of the ground due to great movements deep within the Earth when crustal plates scrape past or pull apart from each other. An earthquake can cause enough damage to buildings to make them collapse

echoes
the indirect sound we hear when vibrations are bounced from an object

eclipse
an eclipse occurs when one planet or Moon shuts out the direct sunlight to another. In an eclipse of the Sun, the Moon passes between the Sun and the Earth, almost blocking it out for several minutes

ecosystem
a balance of plants and animals that has developed in such a way that they have a balanced, self-sustaining and regulating relationship. The largest ecosystems are at the scale of broad areas of natural vegetation such as grasslands

elastic
the way a material will return to its original shape after it has been stretched, squashed or deformed in some other way. Rubber is a good example of an elastic material

electrical conductor
a substance that allows electricity to flow freely through it. Metals are the most common conductors of electricity, although other substances, especially water, can

also readily act as conductors. This is the reason why it is dangerous to have kitchen plugs and switches near to places where water may be splashed or spilled or where the plugs and switches may be touched with wet hands

electromagnet
a form of temporary magnetism produced whenever an electric current flows in a wire. Temporary magnetism is very useful for operating switches by remote control

element
a substance that cannot be broken down into simpler substances by chemical means. Pure chemical substances (such as oxygen or iron) are called elements. Combinations of elements make up the entire known Universe of which 92 are stable and occur naturally

elevators (aeroplane)
these are small flaps in the tail of an aeroplane. Even small changes in the tail will make a big change in direction of the aeroplane. This is why both the elevators and the rudder controls are placed in the tail

embryo
an animal in the early stages of development and after the fertilised cell has begun to divide. After 8 weeks development a human embryo is called a foetus

energy
a property which allows work to be done. The several forms of energy can be converted into each other. Converting stored energy into movement energy is used in starting and moving, whereas converting movement energy into heat energy (through the use of brakes) results in stopping
    chemical: the power in food locked away as chemicals. We release the energy during digestion;
    electrical: the electrical power that is available to make appliances work;
    light: the energy in light waves that plants can use to grow

equator
the line that divides the Earth equally in two and is half way between the poles.

equinox
a time when the length of the day and night are the same. An equinox happens when the Earth is at its shortest distance from the Sun, in March and September

erosion
the breakdown of rock by water, wind, frost and ice and its transport to some other location where it may well be formed into new rock

evaporation
the process whereby liquid water is lost from the surface of plants, the ground and the oceans and becomes water vapour. The energy to change liquid water into moisture comes primarily from the Sun, which is why the ground dries more quickly on a warm summer's day than a cold winter's day

exploit
to make use of a resource. People have to be careful not to over-exploit resources because they are limited

fabric
a cloth made from fibres by knitting, weaving, felting and a variety of other processes

fat
a substance that the body makes to store energy. It is one of the body's main sources of fuel

felting
a special process of matting wool, cotton and other materials so they make a dense waterproof material. Felting is done using both heat and pressure

ferment
the process of rotting through the action of bacteria and fungi

fertilise (fertilize)
the process of bringing female and male parts together in order to produce new life. When fertilisation takes place in a flower the contents of the pollen grain join with the contents inside the flower to make a seed

fertilised egg
a female sex cell that has been united with a male sex cell to make an egg that can grow into a new plant or animal

fibre
a natural or synthetic strand, or filament, of material

>**material**: materials that may be spun into a thread. There are many fibres that are used in fabrics, from the thin strands of glass that make fibre-glass to the delicate fibres off sheep and goats that make wool
>**food**: materials that are found in plants but which are indigestible
>**plant**: plant tissues are made of a material called cellulose. The bark and trunks of trees are hard forms of cellulose which, when treated with chemicals, separate out into fibres

field of view
the total region that can be seen. In people, the field of view is made up of the field from the left eye and the right eye. Together they make a more or less oval field of view, with a 'blind area' just in front of the nose

filament
the fine wire that is used in light bulbs. The wire is made of a special metal that will not easily melt even when it becomes white hot. Because the metal would burn away in air, a filament is placed in a glass bulb with a gas called argon

fission
the process whereby the energy in radioactive substances such as plutonium and uranium is rapidly released to make heat

fleece
the coat of wool that covers a sheep or goat. The wool is not naturally straight, but has a natural crinkly shape which stands up even after it has become wet. A fleece is also covered with natural oils to help keep the hairs waterproof

floppy disk
a small disk used to store magnetic information for a computer

fluid
the general name for either a liquid or a gas. A fluid will change shape to fit inside a container. Pressure can be transferred through a liquid, and this is used in automobiles when the driver puts a foot on the brake. Liquid is forced along a tube and as it presses against brake pads attached to the other end of the tube, the brakes are applied

fluoresce
to give off a glow. Fluorescent tubes glow when an electrical current passes through the gas in the tube. Fluorescent tubes use four or five times less energy than an ordinary bulb for the same light output

flute
a woodwind instrument without a mouthpiece. Sound is made by blowing across a mouth hole

focus
the region that can be seen clearly and where all objects appear to have sharp outlines. Special muscles within the eye pull the lens into different shapes so that we can focus on objects at different distances

fog
cloud at ground level. In a fog there are so many water droplets that it is impossible to see more than a few tens of metres

food chain
the many animals and plants that live together in a balance, the higher members being dependant on the lower as a source of food in some way

force
objects do not move without the application of effort. Perhaps the effort is pulling or pushing. There are many kinds of effort. Each one is a force. In honour of the scientist Newton, who developed the Laws of Motion, force is measured in units called Newtons

formula
an expression which describes a rule of some kind

fossil
the remains of an organism that has been buried in a rock and its form preserved in a recognisable way. It may consist of a cast, a mould or as altered tissue and bone

fossil fuel
a source of concentrated stored energy that was produced millions of years ago during the fossilisation of plants and animals. The main fossil fuels and coal, oil and natural gas

frequency
the number of waves passing each second. It is usually measured in hertz. The note middle C is 256 hertz

friction
the natural stickiness between any two objects in the Universe. Friction occurs because all objects have a natural roughness, even though they may appear smooth to the naked eye. There is a limit to the friction that can oppose movement. A liquid, called a lubricant, placed between two surfaces can help to keep them apart and reduce the value of friction. The driving force needed to overcome friction for a stationary object is higher than that needed for a moving object, which is why engines must develop their greatest power for starting

frond
the feathery leaf of a fern. On the underside can often be found brown spots which release spores

frost
air or ground temperature that falls below 0° C

frostbite
when it is very cold, the blood vessels in the skin get smaller. Under extreme conditions, the blood vessels may get so small that they stop blood from carrying oxygen to the skin and the cells begin to die

fuel
a source of concentrated energy that gives out power when it is burned or changed chemically in some way such as when food is eaten or as a source of heat or power

fundamental
the natural pattern of vibration of an object such as musical pipe. This is the lowest of a series of notes that the pipe can make

fungi
a primitive kind of plant that does not bear flowers or develop proper seeds, but which distributes spores. Mushrooms and many moulds are fungi. They cause dead tissue to rot

fur
the coat of fine hairs that cover many animals such as cats and dogs. Fur has the same purpose as the fleece of a sheep; it helps to keep the animal warm and dry

fuselage
the name given to the body of the aeroplane. The fuselage is usually cigar-shaped and it is braced to take the weight of the wings and tail

gale
wind that is severe enough to capsize small boats at sea

gamelan
an Asian (Indonesian) orchestra which consists mainly of xylophone-type instruments and bells

gas
a substance that is a vapour. Many gases, such as oxygen, are invisible. The main gases of the air are nitrogen, hydrogen and oxygen

gastric juices
the chemicals the body makes in order to break down the food we eat

gears
a set of different sized toothed wheels that interlock in such a way that different amounts of starting advantage can be obtained. During starting, when the greatest advantage is needed, a small wheel on the engine side of the gears is used to drive a large one on the machine

gene
the strings of coded chemical packets that provide a blueprint for life

germanium diode
germanium is a brittle grey-coloured material that was mainly used as part of an electronic circuit for detecting radio waves or in computers

germinated
when seeds sprout into life they are said to have germinated

geyser
geysers are springs that send powerful jets of steam and water into the air from time to time. They are found in places where rocks quite close to the surface have been heated, and they are found in areas as volcanoes or where volcanoes were once active. The name comes from Geyser, a hot fountain in Iceland.

gills
these are the special structures that allow fish and some other animals to absorb oxygen out of the water. Gills do the same job as lungs in land animals

glands
a group of cells which have become specialised for the purpose of producing some special chemical made from parts of the blood. Glands include those for releasing saliva in the mouth, sweat from the skin, and digestive juices inside the gut

gravity
this is the force produced by every object in the Universe.

> The force of gravity depends on the size of the object. If the object is the size of a marble, the gravity force it has is too tiny to notice. But when the object is the size of a planet, its force of gravity force is huge. Suns (which are far bigger than planets) produce the most

powerful gravitational forces. The only exception to this is a collapsing star, which often has a small size but produces an enormous gravitational force. All the stars and the planets in the Universe are thought to have been pulled into shape by gravity. On Earth gravity pulls all objects towards the centre of the planet. A plumb line will therefore always point towards the Earth's centre. Many animals make use of gravity to give them a sense of balance

Green Revolution
the introduction of special high-yielding varieties of crops and modern farming methods to developing countries

Greenhouse Effect
when fossil fuels such as coal, oil and natural gas are burned they release a gas called carbon dioxide. This gas occurs naturally in the air, but the amount has doubled this century due to burning fossil fuels primarily by power stations and motor vehicles. Carbon dioxide traps heat and makes the atmosphere warmer. The way it works is often said to be similar to the way a greenhouse warms up, so people call it the Greenhouse Effect

grid
a network of cables that allow power stations to be linked to homes. A grid allows electricity to be shared, so the power can be sent to wherever it is needed. The tall pylons crossing the countryside carry cables that are part of the power grid

hail
a mixture of ice and water in the form of a ball-shaped lump. Hailstones only fall from thunderclouds

hard disk
a disk made from aluminium and coated with magnetic material

hardness
the way materials can stand up to wear, scratching or being marked.

Materials can be grouped into various degrees of hardness. A scratching tool, for example a glass cutter, has to be very hard, and the best ones have diamond tips, although special steels can also be used

hardware

In computing terms the hardware comprises all the physical parts of a computer, such as the keyboard, the monitor, the logic board and the printer

hardwood

hardwood trees have trunks with very closely packed fibres. This makes the wood dense and hard. Hardwoods are particularly useful for furniture and buildings because they do not easily rot or take up water. Hardwood trees grow very slowly and they are therefore hard to replace

harmonics

the notes that a musical instrument can make that are higher than the fundamental. If the fundamental for a pipe produces a single standing wave, then the first harmonic is produced by making two waves form in the pipe, the second harmonic by making three waves form in the pipe and so on. The number of waves in the pipe is controlled by changing the length of the pipe such as by closing or opening finger-holes on a recorder

harp

a string instrument held upright while the strings are plucked

harpsichord

a piano-like keyboard instrument where the strings are plucked

herbivore

an animal, such as a cow, a rabbit or an elephant, that gets all of its food needs from plants. People are not herbivores because they can choose to eat meat or plants. People fall into the group called omnivores

hibernate

a period of winter rest in an animal's life. During this time the animal is almost completely inactive. It breaths just fast enough to keep it alive

hormone

a hormone is a chemical messenger which is made in a special gland. There are glands scattered all over the body. However, some glands in women and men are different and this is what causes them to develop differently as they become grown-ups

horn (musical)

a tube-like instrument. It was originally a hollowed out animal horn

household circuit

the household circuit is the main electricity supply in the home. It consists of an alternating current. Each country has its own standards for household supply voltage. The most common voltages used are 230 V and 110 V

hurricane

a word for a tropical storm

hydroelectric

a term meaning water-driven. Hydroelectric power is obtained by damming water in a reservoir and then releasing it in a tunnel. Inside the tunnel is a wheel called a turbine, that is turned by the rushing water. The wheel turns the shaft of a generator which in turn makes electricity

Ice Age

the time, beginning about a million years ago, when the Earth cooled down and glaciers spread to make ice sheets that eventually covered nearly a third of the world's land surface

igneous rock

a rock that is made with crystals and which formed from molten magma that rose to the surface from the mantle, perhaps through volcanic vents or through lines of weakness in the crust

illusion

something which deceives the brain by giving a false impression. There are many illusions which are used to advantage: for example, a mirror gives the illusion that the images seen in the mirror are as far behind it as the real objects are in front

image

> **drawing**: a representation of an object.
> **optics**: when light rays are bounced off a mirror, or bent through a lens, they show a picture of the objects they 'see'. This picture is called an image. In relation to eyes an image is brought into focus on the back area of the eye called the retina

imperial system

an internationally-recognised system of measurements. The main units for measurement are the foot (ft) for length, the quart (qt) for volume, the pound (lb) for weight, the second (s) for time, the ampere (A) for electric current, and the degree Fahrenheit (F) for temperature

implant

to attach firmly

incandescent

the light that is produced when a solid, such as a wire in a lamp, is heated

incisor

these are the sharp, chisel-shaped teeth at the front of the mouth. Their job is to cut into the food so that pieces can be torn off

industrial revolution

the time, beginning in Britain in the eighteenth century and lasting through the nineteenth century, when the factory system was developed

industrialise

to move from a society in which many objects are made by hand, and in which crafts and self-sufficiency play an important role, to one where articles are mass-produced by machine and where people become much more dependent on each other

ingredients
the foods that go to make up a mixture. The ingredients of a cake, for example, may be flour, water, fat, salt and cherries

inherit
to gain a characteristic passed on through the genes

inorganic material
any material that does not contain the element carbon

insulator
a substance that does not conduct electricity very well. Most rocks, plastics and plant materials such as wood are good insulators. The air is also a good insulator which is why bare electrical supply cables can be hung from pylons. An insulation is a covering of material that is designed to keep heat or electricity in or out. Insulation is used in the walls of many houses to keep them at a more even temperature, and to save the energy that would be needed for either heating or air conditioning. Plastic insulation is used to protect electrical cables

jet
this is a form of engine which works by igniting an explosive mixture of air and kerosene (a form of petrol). The process is similar to the way a car engine works, but the exhaust gases are used directly to drive the aeroplane through the air. Jet engines work best at high altitudes, which is one reason aeroplanes fly as high as possible, often at about 13 000 metres

jet lag
people who make plane journeys have to wait for their biological clocks to adjust to local time - an effect travellers know as jet lag

kaleidoscope
the name given to a toy that uses several mirrors all facing inwards. The kaleidoscope produces many images of any object placed inside and this may give many new patterns

key stones
the centre stone of an arch made of blocks. Key stones are wedge-shaped so that they will fit round a curve

kilowatt (kW)
this is a unit of power. A one bar electric fire produces an output of about 1 kW of heat per second

landfill
the name given to rubbish that is dumped in an open pit, such as a disused quarry

larva (plural larvae)
the early stage in the life of many insects. Caterpillars are the larvae of moths and butterflies. Grubs are the larvae of beetles and flies

laser
a device that produces a beam of very intense light with very sharply defined edges. The most common type of laser beam is a red colour and comes from a crystal of ruby

lens
when light passes through any transparent object that has curved sides the rays of light will be bent. The curved material is then a lens. A lens is used to change the size of things we look at. There are two common types of lens. In the kind called convex, the lens magnifies. You can recognise it because it has bulging sides. In the type of lens called concave the lens makes things smaller. This lens has dished sides

> **lens (of eye)**: the small flexible disc of transparent material in the front of the eye. The lens is responsible for making light rays focus on the back of the eye

lever
this is a long bar which is used to enable people to move a heavy object more easily. The lever is used with a pivot. The lever is placed under the heavy object and over the pivot. The object is lifted by pressing down on the free end of the lever

lift (in flight)
the force that carries a flying object upwards when it moves through the air quickly. It was discovered by an Italian scientist named Bernoulli. He found that a wing split the air in a special way as it went fast through the air and that this difference caused the wing to lift upwards

light
a special form of energy that can be seen. Light energy can travel through space, which is why the Sun can still give energy to our world even though the Sun and Earth are over 150 million kilometres apart

lightning
the spark that occurs when electricity passes from a cloud to the ground or between layers in a cloud. Fork lightning occurs when you see the spark; sheet lightning is the reflection of the spark

long-sighted
a disorder of the eye which means that the muscles cannot pull the lens far enough for a person to be able to see short distances clearly. This disorder is corrected by the use of contact lenses or spectacles

lubricant
any substance that will remain between two touching surfaces, helping to fill in the natural dips in a surface and therefore make it easier for two objects to slip past one another

luminous
a material that glows when certain types of light shine on it, or which gives out light because of the way magnetism affects it

lunar
anything that relates to the Moon. A lunar month is the time it takes for the Moon to change from new Moon through full Moon and back to new Moon again

magma
the name for molten material that wells up from the mantle whenever a weakness occurs in the Earth's

crust. Magma makes lava, ash, granite, basalt and other rocks depending on how it erupts and whether it erupts on an ocean floor or through a thick slab of continent

magnetic
a material is magnetic when it has the ability to attract iron objects to it. Magnets have places where their magnetic effect is concentrated called magnetic poles. In a magnetic catch the pole of a magnet is placed so that it faces the strip of iron on the door

magnetic disks
circles of material, usually plastic or aluminium, which have a coating of fine iron particles and which are used in computers to store information. Disks that are shared between computers are often called floppy disks

mammal
an animal that gives birth to live offspring (as opposed to, for example, laying eggs). People are mammals, as are deer, squirrels and many other warm-blooded animals with a skeleton of bone, a skin with hairs and which is raised on milk when it is very young

mantle
the processes that go on inside planets normally produce several different layers. The inner layer is called the core, the outer layer is called the crust. The layer between the core and the crust is called the mantle. Not much is known about the mantles of the other planets in the Solar System, but the Earth's mantle is thought to be made of materials rather like the basalt lava that makes up much of the rocks on the ocean floors

manufacture
the industrial processing of materials to make them into new shapes

manufactured goods
any objects that have been made by machine. Most manufactured goods are designed to be easy to make and to assemble. Normally they are

a mixture of several types of materials. This makes them very difficult to recycle

mass
this is the amount of matter in an object. Scientists use the word mass to talk about the amount of matter in an object because its weight changes with the force of gravity. A ball has the same mass on the Earth and on the Moon, but its weight will be much greater on the Earth where gravity is stronger. In regions of space distant from stars and planets, there is very little gravity and substances are then 'weightless' even though they keep the same mass.

mass-produced
the manufacture of many standard items on a factory production line

mate
the sexual partner of an animal

mature
when a plant or animal has grown to its full size

meanders
the regular twists and turns of a river. Most meanders are formed on the flat land at the bottom of a valley

measuring cylinder
a tall glass or plastic vessel with straight sides and marked off in units of volume

mechanical
anything that relates to machines

mesh
the name given to the size of holes between the strands of a net. The size of the mesh is very important in fishing nets, for example, because a big or coarse mesh allows small fish to escape and continue to grow

metamorphic rock
a rock that has been heated or crushed during mountain building sufficiently to change its character. Slate is a common metamorphic rock. Most metamorphic rocks are very hard

metamorphosis
a complete change that happens to an animal as it grows up to be an adult. The word metamorphosis is used only for dramatic changes such as caterpillar to insect or tadpole to frog

meteorite
Small pieces of rock travelling through space are called meteoroids. They are smaller than asteroids but bigger than dust. It was meteorides that originally made up the planets in the Solar system. The Earth draws meteorides towards it all the time. Most of them weight just a few kilogrammes and as they burn up in the atmosphere they give shooting stars or meteors which we see as a trail of light in the night sky. It is rare for a meteorite to land on the Earth's surface before they burn up entirely, but if they do the rocky body that creates a huge crater on impact is called a meteorite

metric system
an internationally-recognised system of measurements based on the decimal system. The main units for measurement are the metre (m) for length, the litre (l) for volume, the kilogram (kg) for weight, the second (s) for time, the ampere (A) for electric current, and the degree Celsius (C) for temperature. The metric system is used throughout the world for scientific measurements even though many countries still maintain an Imperial system for everyday measurements

microbes
a general term used in this book for all microscopic organisms that may cause harm if they are left to multiply in food

microscopic
very tiny, needing a microscope to be seen clearly. Many receptors, such as the cells used for touch, taste and sight, are microscopic in size, but they can still provide large amounts of information for the

brain. Usually objects smaller that a tenth of a millimetre need to be looked at with a microscope

migrate
the long distance movement that some animals make each year in order to find new sources of food. Migrations are most common in areas that experience strong seasonal problems, such as a summer drought or a harsh winter. A bird called the Arctic Tern makes the incredible migration of 17 600 kilometres between its breeding grounds in the Arctic and the Antarctic

mineral
a naturally occurring substance in the Earth, such as chalk or iron, that can be used as a nutrient for plants or as a resource for people. People in industry think of a mineral as a substance that can be dug from the ground and which can be used to make things when it has been properly processed. Clay, limestone and sand are common examples

mirror
most mirrors are made of glass with a layer of silver painted on to the back to give the reflecting surface

mist
a thin form of fog. Usually you can see for more than a hundred metres but you cannot see any distant object

moisture
water vapour in the air

molar
the back teeth which are broad and designed to crush food. The ridges of the upper molars fit closely into the valleys of the lower molars. You can feel this close fit when you rub your teeth together

molecule
the smallest possible particles of a substance. Everything around us, including ourselves, is made of molecules

momentum
a property of an object which causes it to keep moving even when the driving force stops. The amount of momentum varies with the speed and the mass of the object, so fast moving, heavy objects have a greater momentum than slow moving lightweight ones

monitor
the display unit for a computer. The monitor display usually looks like a television screen

mortar
a mixture of cement and sand and lime that makes a fine paste suitable for cementing building blocks together

movement energy
otherwise known as kinetic energy, movement energy is gained as stored energy is lost. So, for example, a vehicle moves (has movement energy) so long as it burns a fuel (and therefore loses stored energy)

moult
a period when animals loose all, or a large part, of their coats or skin. Dogs moult by shedding many hairs, snakes moult by shedding their entire skin

mucus
a slimy liquid that is released from special glands and which can be used as a lubricant

muscles
the tough, stretchy tissues that surround your bones. Muscles can only shorten (tighten), so two sets of muscles are needed around every joint. A great deal of energy is needed to shorten a muscle. Muscles are under the control of nerves, which is why they can react so quickly

musical scale
a series of notes arranged in order

nectar
a scented, sugary solution produced by many flowers and which attracts insects, birds or bats. As the animal sips the nectar it brushes against the flower, bringing in pollen to fertilise the plant and taking more pollen away to fertilise other plants

nerve
a nerve is a special kind of cell, part of which has become stretched out into the shape of a single long fibre. When a nerve cell is stimulated from outside, perhaps by pressure if it is a nerve in a finger, an electrical signal is generated in the nerve cell and passed by the fibre to the brain. The nerves that connect the eye to the brain are often called the optical nerves. Nerves are extremely sensitive and if touched directly can cause considerable pain

net
the outline of a solid shape drawn onto a sheet of paper

niche
a particularly suitable position in amongst all the other living things in a locality

nocturnal animal
an animal that is active at night and which rests during the day

noise
any loud sound that is thought to be unpleasant

note
a single sound. Notes are often played together to make chords. Pleasing patterns of notes make music

nuclear reaction
nuclear reactions take place when energy is given out by atoms in a special way. Enormous temperatures and pressures may be needed to make nuclear reactions, but when they occur, they release very large amounts of energy. Nuclear reactions are continually taking place inside the Sun

nucleus
the innermost region of a cell

nutrients
the special chemicals that are needed to help build new cells. Plants get their nutrients directly from the soil; animals get nutrients by eating plants or other animals. Nutrients include calcium (from milk), salt and iron (from dark-coloured vegetables)

observatory
a place for the scientific study of space. The world's largest optical observatories are placed on high mountains well away from the pollution of cities so they can get the clearest possible view of space

octave
the difference in pitch between two notes, the upper one being twice as high as the lower

opaque
a material which appears solid and which cannot be seen through. Most objects are opaque

optical discs
a circle of plastic in which there is a pattern of tiny pits. Optical discs are often known as compact discs or CDs

orbit
this is the path made by a body that whirls round a fixed point. A ball on the end of a string makes a circular orbit as it whirls round. Most satellites make a nearly circular orbit as they go round the Earth; the Earth and Moon together orbit the Sun in a path that is much more oval (called elliptical)

ore
any rock that contains useful amounts of metal. Most metals are extracted from their ores by heating in a furnace

organic material
any material that contains the element carbon

organism
a general name for any plant or animal. The word micro-organism is often used to describe the very large number of unseen living things that exist in water and which have no commonly used name

organs
one of the major working parts of the body, such as the heart or the kidney

overloaded
a term meaning that more electrical current is flowing than the system can handle. At home an overloaded system will cause a fuse to blow

overtone
another word that means much the same as harmonic

pan-pipes
South American bamboo pipes that are mounted in sets of differing lengths

parallel circuit
when electrical items such as bulbs are connected in parallel, each item is directly connected to the supply. The current flows from the negative terminal to the positive terminal through each item at the same time

parallelogram
a rectangular shape that has been distorted so that both opposite pairs of sides are still parallel to each other, but the corners are no longer at right angles

parasite
an animal or plant that lives within or on another – called the host – and from which it receives essential nourishment. The host does not benefit from the presence of a parasite and is often harmed by it

pendulum.
any object that can swing freely under the effects of gravity will make a pendulum. A pendulum has certain important properties including a regular time for each complete swing, known as the time period

percentage
the value of something when expressed as a proportion of one hundred. Thus a half is 50 hundreds or 50 percent and a quarter is 25 hundreds or 25 percent. The symbol % is often used instead of the word percent

percussion
the name for any instrument that makes a sound when it is struck

perennial
a plant that lives for many years

period
the time it takes for a swinging body like a pendulum to complete one complete swing and return to its starting position

peripheral
any piece of computer hardware that is not part of the central computer 'box'. Keyboards, monitors and printers are all peripherals

periscope
a device for reflecting light through two right angles. This makes it possible for an observer to see over obstacles or round corners

petroleum
the general name for the gases and liquid fuels that form in rocks over millions of years. Petrol (petroleum spirit; US, gasoline) is just one refined component of petroleum

photoelectric cell
an electronic device made using a light-sensitive material. When light shines on the material it creates an electric current that can be used to do work such as showing the amount of light entering a camera

photon
a tiny 'packet' of energy radiated by the Sun

photon
this is the smallest possible 'packet' of light. Photons are given out when special changes, such as great heating, take place in atoms. A stream of photons is seen as a beam of light

photosynthesis
the process that plants use whereby they absorb the energy from the Sun in order to build their tissues from water, air and minerals in the soil

pictographs
a representation of a word or group of words made in the form of pictures. Many ancient pictographs were made on the walls of caves. The most widely used pictographs today are the Chinese and Japanese characters used for their written language

pier (building)
a thickened piece of a wall designed to give strength and to stop the wall from falling over

pile
the yarns of a fabric that stand up from the surface of the fabric. Velvet and carpets have a pile. In the case of carpets the pile is made by looping many yarns through a backing sheet

pitch (musical)
the name used to say how high or low a note is

pivot
the place about which an object can rotate. An axle is a common pivot, but anything can act as a pivot. For example, the joints in your body are all pivots, as are the ends of chairs when they are rocked to and fro

placenta
a piece of special tissue that is attached to the inside of the womb. The baby is attached to the placenta by the umbilical cord

plaque
a substance produced in the mouth. It is a sticky acid substance that makes the food for bacteria. At the same time as eating the plaque, the bacteria eat into the surface of the teeth causing tooth decay. Toothpaste contains substances which balance out the acid and stop bacteria from feeding

plastic
> **material**: these are materials – really called polymers – made mostly from oil and wood-based chemicals. Some can be pushed into a new shape (they are plastic), whereas others break when a force is used (they are brittle). Unfortunately the commonly used word plastic, describing a material, can be confused with the technical word meaning to change shape, which is the reason people have to be careful how they use the word plastic

> **to stretch**: the way material will change shape and remain in that new shape when it is squeezed, stretched or deformed. Steel is plastic because it can be made into new shapes such as cans

pole (magnetic)
the name given to each end of a line. The Earth acts like a long magnet with its ends, or poles, near to the North Pole and the South Pole. As a result the magnetic poles are also called north and south. North and south poles are also used to describe the ends of all other magnets

pollen
a 'dust' made by a flower. Each grain of 'dust' is really a very tiny case containing a substance which is used to fertilise a flower and help make a seed

pollutant
a substance that fouls water. People use the word pollutant to mean the waste chemicals from factories, ships, homes and farms. Together these often spoil water and make it unhealthy and unpleasant

pollution
the release of unnatural quantities of materials into the environment so as to disrupt the normal life processes. Levels of pollutants, such as metals in rivers or acid gases in the air, have built up to dangerous proportions in some parts of the world and urgent action is needed to curb further pollution

polyester
a range of synthetic fibres made originally from oil. Polyester fibres are very springy, so they will always try to spring back to their original straight shape. This is what makes polyesters resist creasing

polymer
any substance that is formed from long linked chains of molecules

polyp
an animal with a hollow cylindrical body with tentacles round the mouth. Many coral animals are polyps. They make a finned chalky frame as they grow. This remains after the animal has died and becomes a permanent part of a coral reef

pores
the surface of the skin has many tiny holes in it. These holes are called pores. Some pores allow fluids, such as sweat, to flow out, others – follicles – provide openings for growing hair

porous
a rock is porous if the tiny mineral particles from which it is made do not fit together completely, leaving gaps that can be filled with water, oil or gas

pot hole
pits that have been formed in the bed of a river by the swirling action of water and pebbles. As the pebbles go round and round in the pot hole, so they wear away the sides and also themselves

power
the rate at which electrical energy is fed into or taken out of a circuit. It is usually measured in watts

precipitation
any form of water or ice that falls from a cloud. It includes rain, hail, drizzle, snow and sleet

precision
something which has a high degree of exactness and accuracy

predator
any animal that kills and eats other animals. Foxes and some beetles are examples of predators

pressure wave
this is the kind of wave that is produced by the human voice or some other source of sound. In a pressure wave the particles move to and from their place of rest. A pressure wave is also called a longitudinal wave because the particles move along in the same direction as the wave

primary colours
the minimum number of colours that, when mixed in the right proportions, can give all the other colours of the spectrum. They are usually red, green and blue

printed circuit
this is a pattern of connections that are made in many pieces of electronic equipment. All the connecting wires are made of flat strips of metal which are stuck down on to a base board. Because they are fixed down there is less chance of mistaking the connections or of the wires breaking

prism
optical: the name of a triangular-shaped piece of transparent material, usually glass. Two of its sides are frequently cut at a right angle. When light enters a prism it is turned back on itself. Prisms are used in binoculars to shorten the length of the sighting tubes. One special property of prisms is to show that white light is really made up of many colours
geometry; a shape with a constant cross section, but which is long in comparison to its section, rather like the shape you get when toothpaste is squeezed from a tube.

projectile
this is any object that is thrown or shot into the air. The projectile might be an arrow, a stone, a ball or a bullet. All make the same type of curving path as they fly through the air

protein
the name given to substances that make the walls of the bodies cells. Young people need to eat a large amount of protein otherwise their growth might be stunted

pulp
the name given to the mashed up fibres of wood or recycled paper. Most pulp made in a factory has been through many chemical stages to get it to an even texture and a desired colour

pupa (plural pupae)
a stage in the life of many insects which is after the larval stage. At this time the insect is enclosed in a bullet-shaped case. Sometimes the pupa is called a chrysalis

pupil (eye)
the dark centre to the eye. The size of the pupil is controlled by changes in the iris, the coloured part of the eye

pyramid
a shape with a square base and four sloping triangular sides that meet in a point. The most famous examples of a pyramid are the Pyramids of Giza, huge burial chambers of the ancient Egyptian kings or pharaohs

quarry
any large pit in solid rock that has been made by people searching for resources in the ground. Chalk, stone and metal ore quarries make some of the world's largest sites for rubbish

quartz
this is a common mineral that makes sand and glass. In its crystal form it is transparent

radar
the equipment used to find planes in the sky. A radio signal is sent out from a transmitter. When it reaches a plane or other solid object some of the waves are bounced back and detected by a receiver. The time it takes for the signal to go out and come back gives the position of the plane

radiate
there are three ways that heat can be transferred: by radiation, conduction and convection. Radiation of the Sun's heat is by sending photons through space. These are then absorbed by the atmosphere, the land and the oceans

radiation
the process of sharing energy between objects separated from one another. Radiated energy travels in waves. Radiation from the Sun consists of a great variety of energy waves, all of which travel at the same speed (that of light)

radioactive
a substance which gives out energy in the form of radiation

random
events in time and space which appear to have no pattern to them. Random events include the numbers produced by chance throws of a pair of dice

range
the value that is obtained when you take the difference between the biggest value and the smallest value of a group of measurements

raw material
a material that is used as the basis of some form of processing

ray (light)
the path followed by light as it moves from its source. Light can be made into rays by putting an obstruction, such as a comb, in front of a beam of light

reach
the distance that a person can comfortably stretch out and still do useful work. Usually reach is less than the furthest part that can be touched because no useful work can be done when fully stretched

receptor
a special kind of nerve cell that turns a sense such as sight, taste, sound or touch, into an electrical signal which is sent to the brain. The receptor cells give the brain all of its information about the outside world. They also feed back information that helps the brain to work organs such as limbs

reconditioned
a machine that has been reconditioned is one where the worn out parts have been replaced. Reconditioning equipment gives a new lease of life and is cheaper than replacing the whole machine

rectangle
a four-sided figure in which all the angles between sides are right angles but where one pair of opposite sides have a different length from the other pair

rectangular
the name for the shape of any block-shaped object. All the angles in a rectangular block are right angles

recycle
to find a new and valuable use for an object or material when it has fulfilled its original function. Recycling often involves the break up and reuse of the original object. In general, far less energy is needed to reuse materials than to make new ones from raw materials

reed (musical)
a small piece of material that vibrates when air is blown across it

refine
to make more pure. A chemical refinery takes a mixture of substances, such as are found in crude oil, and separates out the useful constituents. Metals are refined by taking away impurities. A blast furnace helps to refine iron ore

remote control
most machines are directly controlled by people. Their hands touch the switches on the machine or move wheels, levers, etc. If the controlling is achieved through a cable or by radio then it is said to be under remote control

reproduction
one of the two ways that an animal or plant produces new life similar to itself

reptile
an animal without an in-built way of controlling its body heat. To become active a reptile must absorb energy directly by basking in the sunshine

reserves
the amount of material left in the Earth and which can be extracted by pumping or mining. The amount of reserves often gets larger as people find new ways to extract the desired material

resin
this is a material rather like glue that comes from trees

resonance/resonate
a resonance is a reverberation that is caused by a standing wave developing in the object. Resonance in a vibrating string shows up as a standing wave; resonance in a musical instrument results in one of the notes on the musical scale

resource
a mineral, plant, animal or other substance of the Earth which is used by people to make goods

retina
the part of the eye on which an image is formed after light has passed through the lens. There are millions of tiny light-sensitive cells on the retina surface. Human eyes have both rods (which tell black from white) and cones (which tell about colour). Each rod or cone is a nerve cell that is separately linked to the brain

revolution
one complete turn of a circle

rhythm
the way the music is set out in time

rhythmic
a regular vibration. If a rhythmic vibration is set up it often causes the development of a standing wave

ripple wave
in this kind of wave the particles move up and down (or in small circles in the case of water waves) while the wave moves forwards. It is also called a transverse wave because particles move across, or transverse to, the direction in which the wave moves

rod
any slim cylinder of material which has a stick-like shape

rosin
special sticky material made from turpentine

rotor
the long thin blade set that is fitted to the helicopter. Rotors have special joints at their centre which allow the pilot to change the angle of the blades

saline
Anything that has a lot of salt in it is called saline. Usually the word means that the water has so much salt that it is unfit to drink or will harm plants

saliva
the chemicals that are produced by salivary glands when you begin to eat. Saliva is a mixture of many substances designed to lubricate your food as it goes down your throat. At the same time the chemicals begin to break down, or digest, the food

sand
the smallest pieces of ground-up rock that we can still easily see. Sand is commonly found on beaches, but it is also commonly formed as pebbles, bounced along by rivers, knock pieces from each other or from the river bed

sapling
a young tree. Saplings have supple stems and branches which can easily stand up straight again if they are knocked over. This natural springiness helps the young tree survive trampling by animals

satellite
a body that is trapped in a roughly circular path by the gravity of a larger body. The Earth and other planets are satellites of the Sun. The Moon is the Earth's largest satellite. Most satellites, however, are small machines sent into space to orbit the Earth

saxophone
a reed instrument with a curved and bell shaped end

scan
to glance over quickly. The word is used in computing to mean a machine that sweeps across some information, gathering the data and making it available on a screen

scent
the smell or odour that is created when microscopic particles leave the scented object and become scattered in the air. When scent particles reach the nose they are

dissolved in the mucus and turned into a chemical signal

sediment
the material that settles out at the bottom of an ocean, river or lake and which is made of fine fragments of rock eroded from the land. Sediments eventually become crushed into new rocks, then called sedimentary rocks

sedimentary rock
a rock formed from the deposited remains of other rocks. Most sedimentary rocks form under the seas, their sediments being brought from land by rivers or eroded from cliffs by waves

semi-conductor
a substance such as silicon which can conduct electricity, usually because impurities have been added in a special way. The word is also used to describe a device such as a transistor that depends on the properties of semi-conductor material

shearing
a tearing type of action that happens when two blades close on a material like paper

short circuit
an accidental flow of electricity along an unintentional path

short-sighted
a disorder of the eye which means that the muscles cannot pull the lens far enough for a person to be able to see long distances clearly. This disorder is corrected by the use of contact lenses or spectacles

silicon
a basic substance, or element, of the Universe like lead or oxygen. It is usually found as a component of sand. In its pure form it is a grey solid

skein
a length of yarn that has been wound into a long coil. Skeins are useful ways of storing yarns. Knitting wool is often sold in skeins

skyscraper
a building used as apartments or offices, which is unusually tall and which is made with a frame to hold it up

sleet
a partly melted form of snow

snow, snowflake
ice crystals that have formed into large groups to make a snowflake, and many snowflakes fall as snow

software
the name given to any computer instruction, usually a program

solar
a name given to the Sun. Solar energy is the light energy of the Sun. Plants use this energy to make their tissues. Scientists expect solar energy to become very important as a means of power for people in the next century

Solar System
this is the name given to the group of planets and other bodies that orbit the Sun. Two opposing forces hold all the planets in their orbits. Imagine a ball being whirled around your head on a string. The whirling force which would send the ball far away if you let go of the string is the speed of the planets; the string that holds the ball in place is the force of gravity produced by the Sun. There are nine planets, at least 54 Moons, more than 1,000 comets, and countless asteroids and meteoroids, together with a background of dust

solstice
the time when the Earth is at its greatest distance from the Sun, in December and June each year

solution
the name given to describe the mixture of one substance inside another. A salt solution is made of water and salt, but if the water is boiled away, the salt will reform

sound
a sound is caused when there is a rapid disturbance in air. It may be produced in the throat to give speech or singing, or it may be due

to some other movement such as a loudspeaker vibrating or a balloon exploding

sound barrier
the speed at which a flying object catches up with the sound waves that it produces. People have used the sound barrier as a goal when designing faster and faster planes. The sound barrier is reached at a speed of 322 metres per second

sound box
a form of amplifier that is used to make musical instruments louder

space (astronomical)
the region beyond the Earth's atmosphere containing all the planets and stars. It is often used to mean the Universe except for the Earth

species
a group of plants or animals that can breed among its members. Oaks make a species because pollen from one oak tree can fertilise a flower from another oak

spectrum
the wide range of colours that make up visible light

sphere
a ball-shaped object. Spheres roll easily in any direction and they are used in many bearings

spinning (fibre)
the process of twisting fibres of wool, cotton, hemp and other short fibres together so that they give a long thread or yarn which can then be used to make fabrics. Long fibres such as silk are not spun, but simply wound together to give threads

spirit
a liquid which has been distilled usually by boiling. Spirits flow very easily and do not freeze as easily as water, which makes them suitable to use in levelling devices used in the open

spore
a very tiny grain which contains part of a fungus, moss or fern. Spores will grow readily on damp ground

stall (flight)
this is the steepest angle that a wing can get lift. If the angle of the wing gets steeper the lift will disappear and the wing will no longer be able to keep the body in the air. Stalling can be a major cause of aeroplane crashes

standing wave
this is the wave produced when a wave that has been bounced from a surface exactly matches the next advancing wave

staple
> **food**: foods that are essential to healthy living.
> **crop**: staple crop is one that is used to provide most of the food for a community. Wheat, maize and rice are all examples of staple crops

star
stars are balls of intensely hot liquid and gas. Our Sun is a small star compared with many in the Universe. Stars are so hot that no solid rock can form

starch
one of the common substances in the carbohydrate group. Starches are our most common form of day to day energy

static
a form of electric charge that builds up on the surface of some objects. If the charge gets big enough a spark can jump the gap. Lightning is caused this way

stereophonic
a system for recording and playing sound using two or more microphones and loudspeakers

stethoscope
an instrument consisting of a tube with a flat disc at one end, and a pair of earpieces at the together, connected by a flexible tube. The stethoscope allows sound waves made by pumping blood and other bodily activities to be easily heard by a doctor

stock (food)
a liquid made from boiling animal products such as bones with vegetable remains to get the remaining goodness from them

Stone Age
the earliest time of civilisation, over 3000 years ago, when people mainly used stone implements

stored energy
otherwise known as potential energy because it has the ability, or potential to do some work. A fuel is a source of stored energy

storm force wind
a wind that is so strong it can damage buildings as well as capsize ships at sea

stratus cloud
thick, heavy flat clouds, often with ragged rolls of cloud below. They belong to areas of low pressure and storms

streamline
a streamlined shape is one that has been shaped to give the least drag as an object moves. It is particularly important that fast moving objects, such as aircraft, are streamlined to make sure that they push air or water aside in a smooth fashion, thereby making the effects of friction as small as possible

strength
of a material is a way of describing how well a material will stand up to a stretching, twisting, bending or squashing force without breaking

stress and strain
a stress is the force, such as pulling or pushing, applied over the area of an object. When the material changes shape because of the force, the movement is called a strain

supple
a material that is supple can bend easily without damage. The new shoots on a tree are very supple and will bend over on themselves without breaking, yet they can also stand up straight when no force is applied

surface tension
the way that some liquids such as water behave in the presence of air by having the appearance of an elastic skin. Surface tension keeps water droplets whole instead of spreading out as a film

symmetrical/symmetry
the way many objects are arranged such that they have parts which are the same shape arranged either side of a line or around an axis. For example most bodies are symmetrical about a line drawn from the head to between the legs. A ball is symmetrical about any line that goes through its centre

synchronized
when many items all move in step they are said to be synchronized. Many actions of animals are synchronized, such as walking

synthetic material
any material that is made by people in a factory or workshop and which would not occur naturally. The largest groups of synthetic materials are the polymers (plastics)

tease
the process of gently pulling at a matted collection of fibres so they become loosened and then can be separated. Teasing is an essential first step in spinning

technologist
A person who makes use of scientific discoveries to make goods which can be used. For example, the existence and nature of radio waves was discovered by scientists, but technologists then made use of this natural property to make radio sets that we can all use

terminal
a connector, or socket, fixed to a piece of equipment that allows a cable to be connected to it. In computer usage the word 'port' can also be used. Terminal is also the name given to a computer keyboard and monitor which are linked to a main networked computer and which allows many

people access to the same large computer processing power

territory
the area that an animal tries to keep for its own use. Males will fight over territories because once they have mated, the territory must have enough food to support male, females and offspring

tessellation
a mosaic or pattern built up of many items all with the same shape and which will fit together without leaving any gaps. Triangles are examples of shapes that tessellate, whereas pentagons will not

textile
the general name for any kind of fabric or cloth, but especially when it has been woven

thermal
the rising current of air that allows gliders and birds to get lift. Thermals are strongest on a clear day when the Sun can warm the ground. As some places warm faster than others the air above them warms fast as well. This warm air then becomes light and starts to float upwards, creating a thermal

thermometer
the instrument used to measure temperature. It is marked in degrees Celsius, shown as °C, for short or degrees Farenheit, shown as °F

thunder
the sound that is heard when a flash of lightning occurs. The thunder is made by the air as it is quickly heated by the lightning spark

trait
a characteristic feature of a plant or animal which helps to distinguish it from others of the same species

transducer
a device that changes, for example, a pressure into an electrical signal. Transducers are useful in robotics because they enable a robot to develop a sense of touch

transistor
a small device made of semi-conductor material. It can work as a tiny switch or to make an electrical signal stronger. Thousands of transistors can be placed inside a 'chip', saving space and materials. Transistors are the basic building blocks of a computer system

transmitter
a mechanism that is able to send out information. Our vocal chords are a form of transmitter because they send out sound waves which can be detected by other people

transparent
a material which will allow light to pass through it. Glass and water are examples of transparent materials

treatment plant
a place for processing the polluted waters of rivers or waste-pipes. Treatment works use filters and microbes to get rid of the most poisonous substances. When water leaves a treatment plant it should be good enough to drink

tributary
a tributary is a channel that flows into the main stem of a river system

tropics
the lands that lie either side of the equator and where the Sun shines directly overhead at least once a year

trumpet
a brass wind instrument. The sounds are made by shaping the lips in a special way against the trumpet mouthpiece

turbine
a machine with many blades that

is used to make electricity. Rushing water is used to turn the blades and these in turn cause the shaft of an electric generator to turn. The faster the water flows, the quicker the turbine turns and the more electricity is made

typhoon
a term for a tropical storm

ultrasounds
sound waves which are too high to be heard by humans. Some animals find ultrasounds particularly useful for getting a sense of direction and for finding food

ultraviolet light
this is part of the wide range of light that comes from the Sun. We can only see part of the Sun's radiation. This is called visible light. The type of radiation that is out of our visual range and just beyond violet is called ultraviolet. High levels of ultra-violet radiation is harmful for most plants and animals

unique
the only one of a particular type

Universe
this is the name given to the entirety of everything that we know about. It includes the Solar System, the Galaxy and all other galaxies beyond the reach of our most powerful telescopes

vacuum
this is the absence of matter. An almost complete vacuum exists in space. A true vacuum is almost impossible to achieve, and so it is common to use the word vacuum to describe a space that has had most of the air pumped out of it. The most common near vacuum is found in thermal flasks and in television tubes. If one of these containers is broken the air rushes in and gives the effect of an explosion, scattering pieces of sharp glass. It is therefore dangerous to break vacuum flasks

valve
  mechanical: a flap or other means of blocking the flow of a gas or liquid
  musical: a device which opens and closes over holes in wind instruments. There are many kinds of valve. Some are simple flaps over holes such as in the flute, whereas others are worked by pistons, such as in brass instruments

vein (plants)
the water channels in the leaves of plants. The veins are hollow tubes and so they help to strengthen the plant and make leaves stand stiff

vermin
any creature that may carry disease and which is seen as a pest. Very often it refers to rodents such as rats and mice

vibration
a regular pattern of movements. Sound waves are vibrations

violin
a string instrument played with a bow

vitamins
essential chemicals that the body uses to help prevent illness and in many other essential processes. They are easily destroyed by cooking or storing food. This is why fresh food is so essential

vocal chords
the part of the lower throat that has two flaps of skin that vibrate as air flows over them. The vocal chords are used with the mouth to form many types of sound

volume
the amount of space taken up by an object. Volume is measured by multiplying together the length, breadth and width of an object

water cycle
the never-ending way in which water moves around the world. People normally think of the cycle as starting in the oceans. They then follow the path of the water through clouds and rain, through rocks and soil, to the rivers that return the water to the sea

water repellent
a substance such as grease that will not dissolve in water. A water repellent painted on to a cloth will not let water get to the fibres. Many raincoats are treated with water repellents

water vapour
The kind of water that occurs as an invisible gas, and is often called 'moisture'. The amount of water vapour that can be held in the air gets less at lower temperatures, so a cold day forces much vapour to be turned back to water droplets. This gives dew

wavelength
the length of each complete wave. A wavelength is usually measured from half way between a crest and a trough

weather
the day to day nature of the air. Weather is measured by temperature, windiness, cloud, sunshine and moisture

weaving
the interlacing of threads or yarn to form an interlaced pattern that will not fall apart. This process is still done by hand in many countries, but it can also be done very swiftly by machine. A weaving frame was one of the first machines that started the industrial revolution over two hundred years ago

weed
a weed is a plant that will easily grow at a site but which a gardener or farmer does not want. Weeds are valuable in woodlands because they are quick to cover up a piece of bare ground

weight
objects have a weight due to gravity. A table tennis ball and a lump of lead of the same size will weigh different amounts because of gravity. The weight of an object is measured in units called Newtons

wind
the flow of air over the Earth's surface. Usually it is measured in metres per second

womb
the place inside the female where the baby develops. The womb, or uterus, is a tube-like muscle which is strong enough to push the baby out when it is time to give birth

xylophone
a percussion instrument made of a row of tuned wooden or metal blocks that are hit with sticks

yarn
a continuous twisted strand of fibres produced by a process such as spinning

Index

Aa

Bb

Gg

Hh

Tt